Autism

The Gift That Needs to Be Opened

Tom Jackman

Autism

The Gift That Needs to Be Opened

with a foreword by Senator Jim Munson

Autism Society
Newfoundland and Labrador

FLANKER PRESS LIMITED
ST. JOHN'S

Library and Archives Canada Cataloguing in Publication

Autism : the gift that needs to be opened / with a foreword by Senator Jim Munson ; Autism Society Newfoundland and Labrador.

Includes bibliographical references and index.
Issued in print and electronic formats.
ISBN 978-1-77117-446-6 (paperback).--ISBN 978-1-77117-447-3 (html).--
ISBN 978-1-77117-448-0 (kindle).--ISBN 978-1-77117-449-7 (pdf)

1. Autism spectrum disorders. 2. Autism spectrum disorders--Treatment. 3. Autistic people--Family relationships. 4. Autistic people--Biography. I. Autism Society of Newfoundland and Labrador, author II. Title.

RC553.A88A97 2015 616.85'882 C2015-906294-2
C2015-906295-0

PRINTED IN CANADA

RECYCLED
Paper made from recycled material
FSC® C103567

This paper has been certified to meet the environmental and social standards of the Forest Stewardship Council® (FSC®) and comes from responsibly managed forests, and verified recycled sources.

Cover Design by Graham Blair Edited by Robin McGrath

FLANKER PRESS LTD.
PO BOX 2522, STATION C
ST. JOHN'S, NL
CANADA

TELEPHONE: (709) 739-4477 FAX: (709) 739-4420 TOLL-FREE: 1-866-739-4420
WWW.FLANKERPRESS.COM

9 8 7 6 5 4 3 2 1

Canada Canada Council for the Arts Conseil des Arts du Canada Newfoundland Labrador

We acknowledge the [financial] support of the Government of Canada. *Nous reconnaissons l'appui [financier] du gouvernement du Canada.* We acknowledge the support of the Canada Council for the Arts, which last year invested $153 million to bring the arts to Canadians throughout the country. *Nous remercions le Conseil des arts du Canada de son soutien. L'an dernier, le Conseil a investi 153 millions de dollars pour mettre de l'art dans la vie des Canadiennes et des Canadiens de tout le pays.* We acknowledge the financial support of the Government of Newfoundland and Labrador, Department of Tourism, Culture and Recreation for our publishing activities.

Contents

Foreword

by Senator Jim Munson

Maggie, Kyle, Liam, Olivia, Adrian, Tom, Kara, Matthew, Michael—these individuals are some of the gifts you will meet in this remarkable collection of short stories. Often an invitation to read a book is to describe it as a good summertime read or the perfect Christmas book—but this is a book for all seasons. This is a powerful collection of stories which will likely alter your view and perception of disability and ability.

What comes sharply into focus is the depth and strength of a parent's love for a child or adult with autism. As you turn each page and as you meet each individual, you will feel deeply the true meaning of commitment and care, every day, 365 days of the year.

This wonderful collection leads you into aspects of everyday living: how parents and children act and react, how therapists do their work, and why as a society we have a vital role to play. Their descriptions, clues, and little nuggets of what parents live with every day and teaching tools from experts in the field enrich our understanding of the life and challenges of families.

The story of Maggie brings all of that out vividly. Through her mother's words, this little girl literally jumps off the page. Nicole Parsons writes:

> Maggie had a unique way of twisting words around. My father had taken her to our local Nayler's Beach one day for a little outing. When they had gone about halfway down the sand, Maggie grew tired and wanted to get up in his arms.

> "Carry you me," she said to her grandfather. Maggie's own words would bring us through. Carry you me.

And that's what this book does; it carries you through the isolation, the fears, and the profound and lingering question of parents: why did this happen to us? The gift to readers is that it opens our eyes to the reality of what friends, neighbours, and families live with every day. Through tears and through laughter, every page has a teaching insight and tool for us to use in our understanding of autism.

As I read and reread, I had to stop and take a deep breath after each chapter. Sometimes I was out of breath because I became so emotionally involved in the lives of each family. I would get up and walk around a room holding my thoughts in check. That was my reading experience.

This is mother Laura Hamlyn:

> Autism is simply a word, not who the individual is. It is just part of who they are. I have a daughter with autism and I am proud to call her mine.

The publisher of these pages has found a balance in allowing families to tell their stories in their own words and inviting the experts to share their experience. By doing this, Jerry Cranford is giving us his own gift of what needs to be opened. He presents the stories and we discover how talented the storytellers are.

There is more than the storytelling of different families. The words of an occupational therapist struck a strong chord in me, and I am sure it will with you. Roseanne Hickey-Hatchett in describing her work says:

> The child is very much the leader. The therapist's role is to follow the lead. When we understand the complexity of sensory processing as "a traffic jam in the brain" and we want our children to be joyful, it becomes especially meaningful to seek further knowledge about SPD—sensory processing disorder.

In many respects the gifts on the following pages have already been opened. They just have to be reopened slowly. I found myself drifting back to each short story remembering the words of a parent, a child, an adult.

Why?

You only have to listen to Katrina Bajzak in talking about her son Adrian. And remember, this comes from a mother who when she first heard about the diagnosis sat in her car with "tears flowing."

She writes:

> There are no limits to what a child with autism can do, and Adrian reminds me of this every day. There are still everyday challenges, but with a lot of hard work, love, and faith, these challenges have become much more manageable. This has mainly become possible with advocacy, and this is the biggest piece of advice that I would like to give to parents—do not be afraid to advocate for your child.

I am also an advocate filled with hope. It is by advocating in collaboration with others that our children and adults will truly be able to display the full range of their abilities.

This book is a gift of words, and I will leave it to Tom Jackman, who you will meet in the following pages, to have the final word.

He writes:

> There is no disability, only different ability; you choose how to see it.

What more can be said?

Growing up in Campbellton, New Brunswick, Jim Munson decided at a young age that journalism was the career for him. He loved listening to radio broadcasts and delivering papers that connected him with people, places, and events across the world.

His dream came true, and for more than thirty years he worked as a reporter connecting Canadians with some of the most riveting world events of the last century: the FLQ crisis in Montreal, the assassination of Indira Gandhi, the first Gulf War, the massacre at Tiananmen Square—to name a few. Twice he was nominated for the prestigious Gemini Award.

His career in journalism led to a successful career in communications, which included serving as director of communications for Prime Minister Jean Chrétien.

Jim Munson knows that good government communications is about building relationships between people: politicians, journalists, public servants, and citizens. These skills serve him well in the Senate where, after being appointed in 2003, Jim Munson has served as Caucus Chair and Whip.

Outside the Senate, Senator Jim Munson devotes his energy to his children, the rights of the child, families with autism, Special Olympics, and SOS Children's Villages Canada.

Introduction

Autism is a complex developmental disorder that affects the function of the brain. It is the most common neurological disorder affecting children in Canada. It typically appears in the first three years of life and is a lifelong condition. A person with autism has a normal life expectancy.

Autism prevalence rates increased as much as 17% annually in recent years. At the time of this printing, statistics from the US Centers for Disease Control and Prevention (CDC) identify one in sixty-eight people on the autism spectrum; that represents more than a tenfold increase in prevalence in just forty years.

Autism is the fastest-growing developmental disability today. We know incidence rates among children and youth are still increasing. Currently, there are no means to prevent autism, no fully effective treatments, and there is no cure. Autism can be managed, however, with a variety of effective therapies.

Autism: The Gift That Needs to Be Opened is the story of autism from the vantage points of parents and caregivers of individuals with autism, and those who have autism themselves. They share personal stories that may bring tears of joy. Some stories will make you smile; others may make you cry. But all these true stories will inspire you, while providing increased awareness and knowledge around autism spectrum disorder and those affected by it.

Scott Crocker
Executive Director
Autism Society, Newfoundland and Labrador

Aspies

by Temple Grandin

PHOTO BY ROSALIE WINARD

Temple Grandin, Ph.D. did not talk until she was three and a half years old, communicating her frustration instead by screaming and peeping and humming. Today she is a professor of animal science at Colorado State University and has a long career in the meat industry designing equipment and supervising its construction.

Throughout my life, I have met and worked with many people on the autism spectrum whose condition has gone undiagnosed. Many of them are in technical fields, such as engineering, computer programming, industrial design, and equipment construction. I too am a "techie" and feel that my career is my life. I am what I do. I have observed that "techies" who get into good careers appear to be happier because they are surrounded by "their people." John Robison, in his book *Be Different*, embraces Asperger's syndrome and talks about his good techie life, making special effects for rock bands and learning about electronics from various mentors. At the time of writing this, I was doing lots of public speaking and teaching but not a lot of technical work. In between speaking engagements, I managed to visit a beef plant to fix some equipment problems. It was so much fun being a techie again. I love using my mind to solve problems.

Some of the most important companies in Silicon Valley are led by people on the autism spectrum. Many school systems today would assign a diagnosis of autism to Albert Einstein. He did not speak until the age of three, and he demonstrated many odd behaviours that are attributed to autism. At an autism meeting, a retired NASA space scientist walked up to me and said that he was sure many of his colleagues were on the autism spectrum. Several books have been written that profile famous scientists and musicians who were likely on the spectrum, as well.

Aspie Friends in College

Life was really difficult for me in both college and graduate school. I did not fit in with the other students. The saying, "Birds of a feather flock together," rang very true. During this time, I had several friends whom I believe were on the spectrum but were undiagnosed. My college years were very difficult emotionally. These friends kept me going when I felt depressed. Through the years, I have maintained contact with the friends I made then. Some of them endured many difficulties, but they all managed to support themselves and remain employed. These people were some of the few who sought me out and made an effort to be my friend.

Tim, a short, nerdy kid who loved CB (Citizens' Band) radios, invited me to join his CB club. Nobody else at my college shared Tim's enthusiasm for CB radios or emergency communication. Tim saw me as a kindred spirit who could share his interest in CB radios. We had a great time going to CB Club meetings off campus. Tim went on to become an emergency medical technician, or EMT, and today, he runs an ambulance company.

The physical education teacher, Mrs. Estes, also sought me out. She was the weird lady on campus who wore long johns under all her skirts and put together strange mixtures of clothes. When I felt lonely, I often went over to her house just to talk. When I graduated, she gave me a little card and told me that it was a "phone card" I could use to call her anytime if I ever needed advice. Today, if Mrs. Estes were a child, I think she would likely receive a diagnosis of Asperger's. Mrs. Estes was married to another faculty member and had children, as well.

In graduate school, I became friends with two people who were definitely on the autism spectrum. One of them received a Ph.D. in history, and every year, I receive a card from him. He has been underemployed all his life in specialty retail. He has held three jobs since he graduated in the mid-1970s. One job he lost when the business closed, and his present job, at a large specialty retailer, has been stable for years. Specialty retail is a good job for a "non-techie" type because the employee is appreciated for his or her keen knowledge of the merchandise. Examples of specialty retailing are hardware, men's clothing, sporting goods, electronics, computers, jewellery, books, and furniture. I can also remember the Aspie guy who worked for years at the local hardware store. He knew everything about paint. Everybody laughed at the goofy Superman advertisements he did at the local TV station. It was "Bobby to the rescue for your painting problems."

Aspies in My Workplace

I have worked with all kinds of technical people who are on the autism spectrum but have never received a diagnosis. They have adapted better than some of the people in this book and therefore didn't feel a need for a diagnosis. The reason why the contributors sought out a diagnosis as older adults was because of the serious problems they continued to face. When I first started my career, I often got lonely, and I would go down to the Armour Corporate Center in Phoenix to talk to Sam. Sam was an engineer, and his workmates would say, "You ask Sam what time it is, and he will tell you how to build a watch." It was so much fun to talk to Sam about building meat plants. He was definitely on the spectrum, and he held a high-level engineering job and frequently visited the meat plants. When I was fully engaged with individuals who loved to talk about engineering, animal behaviour, or cattle, I was happy, and I forgot about the emotional difficulties.

Some of the people I work with on my design projects have a certain degree of autism. One, an excellent specialty metal fabricator, has worked on many of my projects. He has a small shop and builds conveyors for many major meat companies. He called me one day all upset because a plant manager had been really mean to him. He told me the entire story, and it became obvious that the manager was using him and had no intention of paying for the equipment he "bought." I understood his frustration and was able to help. I told him that the guy was a jerk and that the best thing to do was to quietly remove the equipment and walk away. I reminded him that he had many good clients and that he needed to concentrate on them. I told him to work with the many other clients who appreciated his excellent, innovative work.

Temple Grandin's book Emergence: Labeled Autistic *is a book which stunned the world because, until its publication, most professionals and parents assumed that autism was virtually a death sentence to achievement and productivity in life. (Note: Names of friends in this story are changed to protect confidentiality).*

Reprinted from *Different . . . Not Less: Inspiring Stories of Achievement and Successful Employment from Adults with Autism, Asperger's, and ADHD* with permission by Temple Grandin.

Daily Inspiration

by Katrina Bajzak

Katrina Bajzak was born and raised in the province of Newfoundland and Labrador, Canada. She received her Bachelor of Arts (French) from Université Laval in Quebec City and her Bachelor of Education (Intermediate/Secondary) from Memorial University of Newfoundland. She also received her Masters degree in French language and literature from Memorial University of Newfoundland. Shortly after completing her post-secondary education, Katrina and her husband moved to the State of Qatar in the Middle East for five and a half years, where she was an English as a Foreign Language (EFL) instructor with the College of the North Atlantic (CNA)—Qatar. Katrina felt it was a truly unique experience to meet so many wonderful foreign students and expatriate friends and feels blessed to have had the opportunity to travel the world. She returned to Newfoundland from the Middle East in 2009, and shortly after her return she was re-employed by CNA as a Communications/ESL instructor. In 2011, Katrina and her husband were blessed with the birth of two beautiful boys. In the summer of 2013, one of their twin boys was diagnosed with autism.

July 27, 2013. It's a day I'll never forget; it's the day I found out that my son had autism. As we were leaving a private clinic in Nova Scotia after receiving his diagnosis, I felt such an array of emotions, but the first thought that ran through my mind was "Katrina, don't cry. You are stronger than this." I just felt at that moment that I had to keep it together, even though we had just been given what we thought of at that time as devastating news. I couldn't cry in front of my son, because I was his mom and I didn't want him to think that anything was wrong. Furthermore, I feel that moms are protectors, and I didn't want to show any signs of weakness in front of him. To be honest, I don't know if I could have cried. I just felt numb. When it comes to difficult situations in life, I am the kind of person who always believes in preparing for the worst but, at the same time, hopes for the best outcome. I had tried to prepare myself for the possibility that my son might be autistic, but nothing can prepare a parent to hear that type of news.

When my husband and I left the clinic, we just stood in the parking lot. We didn't say much to each other, but we didn't have to. We both looked lovingly at our little boy, who was wearing the cutest frog raincoat and matching rain boots. He was contentedly wandering around the parking lot picking up small stones and examining them. For him, nothing in his life had changed, but for us, our world had just been turned upside down. Adrian was twenty-two months old at the time of his diagnosis. How exactly was his diagnosis going to affect his young life? He wasn't even two years old yet and I felt as though we had all been given a life sentence.

I started to think about what his diagnosis might mean for his life in the future. I wondered if he would ever be able to talk, play with other children, go to school or university, and live independently. I didn't realize it at the moment, but I now realize that most mothers inherently have their children's lives planned out from the moment of conception. It isn't necessarily a plan that is written out, but usually mothers have an internal plan of what their children's lives will be like from childhood until they leave home. I felt as though I were driving down a straight highway and suddenly came upon a sharp turn in the road and had to slam on the brakes. I did not expect this, and it left me feeling shocked, saddened, angry . . . I felt robbed of the life that I had planned for my child.

However, I guess that's the funny thing about life; there are always sharp twists and turns, and we don't always get notice of when they are about to happen, but we eventually have to learn to accept them. I knew that I had to find a way to process and accept Adrian's diagnosis, but I had no idea where to start. In addition to how Adrian's diagnosis would affect him, we had another important variable to consider, the fact that Adrian had an exuberant, inquisitive, and fearless twin brother. How was Adrian's diagnosis going to affect his brother, Krisztian, and our entire family?

My husband and I were elated when we found out that we were having twins. We were also apprehensive, as twin pregnancies can by nature be more risky than singleton pregnancies. I prayed every day that my little baby boys would be safe and that I could carry them to a point where they would have a reasonable chance of survival. According to my obstetrician, the babies would be viable at twenty-eight weeks of gestation, so my primary goal was to make it to twenty-eight weeks. I was lucky in the sense that I had a relatively uncomplicated pregnancy. When I made it to twenty-eight weeks, I was just so happy to be able to get to this point that I allowed myself to relax a little and be grateful for every additional day that I could keep them in their warm, comfortable environment. At around thirty weeks, my obstetrician informed me that Baby A (babies are defined as Baby A and Baby B in twin pregnancies) was breech and that, if he didn't move to a head-down position, the babies would have to be delivered via Caesarean section. Baby A was Adrian. My doctor informed me that she would schedule a C-section for me at thirty-six weeks in the eventuality that Baby A didn't turn.

The thought of a C-section was daunting. However, I kept trying to focus on the fact that the health of the babies was of the utmost importance. I knew that I really had no control over the situation; nature simply had to take its course. In the back of my mind, I never really thought that I would make it to thirty-six weeks, but I did, and on September 14, 2011, Adrian and Krisztian were born by C-section, weighing 6.1 and 6.2 pounds, respectively. They were perfectly healthy babies and they didn't have to spend a single day in the NICU. We felt truly blessed.

During the first nine or ten months of the boys' lives, everything was great. They were growing and gaining weight, and all checkups with our pediatrician led us to believe that we had two happy and healthy boys. However, around eleven months of age, my husband began to notice peculiarities with Adrian. He was the first to notice that Adrian didn't respond when we called his name. At first I wasn't overly concerned about this, as I felt that he was probably just overly interested in what he was doing. At the time I didn't really consider this to be a red flag because I could relate to Adrian's behaviour as I, myself, have a tendency to tune out distractions when I am on a task. However, as time progressed, we became more concerned. More often than not, he just wasn't responding to his name.

Another behaviour that we began to notice was the fact that he wasn't playing with toys functionally. Instead, he would pick up an object, examine it, and focus on manipulating it. One toy that I remember in particular was a lighted ball. Adrian wasn't interested in rolling the ball with his brother. He was more interested in self-play and enjoyed dropping the ball and holding it up close, examining it from different angles when it lit up. He was also interested in the patterns in the rugs that we had brought home from the Middle East, and he would follow the pattern lines with his fingers. Similarly, he enjoyed touching the grout lines between ceramic tiles, paying attention to their texture and linear features.

As a mother of two young children, I was often exhausted, and I revelled in the fact that Adrian was able to entertain himself. In so many ways, he was such a good baby in that he didn't demand much attention. It became habitual for me to let him "do his own thing," particularly as I had another child who wanted me to engage in activities with him.

Over time I noticed Adrian's level of self-play and his lack of interest in interacting with others, especially his twin brother. Krisztian made several attempts to play with his brother and gauged his interest, but Adrian didn't reciprocate or demonstrate any interest in engaging in any playful activities with him. People kept telling me that the best aspect about having twins was that they would be able to entertain each other. With my twins, there were no signs of this happening at all. Oftentimes I played with Krisztian; I felt sorry that he was not getting the appropriate level of play required to enhance his own social developmental needs. That's the difficulty about twins. It's a mother's natural instinct to compare them because they are the exact same age. It's important to realize that twins may have similarities, but they are also individuals. I tried to be cognizant of this when comparing my sons to each other. Adrian was not as advanced developmentally as Krisztian, but I tried to keep an open mind and remind myself that, even though they were twins, they were entitled to have different personalities, abilities, and interests. I felt that Adrian was just a little behind, and perhaps he was developing a little differently than Krisztian. Maybe I was reading too much into things. As well, I believed at the time that being quirky or different wasn't necessarily a defect.

I addressed some of these concerns with my family doctor. She attempted to be reassuring by reminding me that twins tend to have more development issues than singletons and that boys develop differently than girls, particularly when it comes to speech. Speech was another area of concern. Krisztian was attempting to make some simple sounds like "ma ma" and "da da," but Adrian was not speaking at all.

The next important thing happened when I took my sons to get their twelve-month immunizations and checkup. In addition to their needles, the public health nurses performed a version of the Denver Developmental Screening Test. This test assesses childhood development in language/cognitive skills, fine motor skills, and gross motor skills to ensure that they are meeting the goals for their age. My husband and I were informed that Adrian failed this test in all areas. In terms of language/cognitive skills, he was not imitating sounds, saying single syllables, or putting syllables together. In terms of fine motor skills, he was not able to do tasks such as picking up two cubes and putting them in a cup. As for gross motor skills, Adrian still wasn't walking, which is not completely unusual for a twelve-month-old, but he couldn't stand on his own without support, either. Additionally, he wasn't using simple gestures such as waving goodbye.

At this point the pubic health nurses weren't telling us that they suspected autism; they didn't have the necessary training to make this assessment. They simply told us that there were developmental delays in all areas, so it was their responsibility to refer us to other specialists, so that the reasons behind these delays could be determined. We were sent to four different specialties: physiotherapy (which had a one-month wait-list), speech pathology (a twelve- to sixteen-month wait-list), pediatrics (a twelve-month wait-list), and occupational therapy (a two-year wait-list). Luckily, we were able to see a physiotherapist quickly, and that appointment was encouraging. Adrian was making all the proper movements toward being able to walk; we just needed to do some extra exercises with him at home to help strengthen his leg muscles. Unfortunately, we would have to wait a little longer to see the other specialists.

After reflecting upon the results of this assessment, we booked an appointment with our family doctor in January 2013. We had definite concerns of autism considering the fact that Adrian had challenges in many areas and was making limited eye contact with people. Luckily, our family doctor was able to obtain an appointment for us with a pediatrician with only a five-month wait; this was a much better scenario than the twelve-month wait that we had expected. At our first meeting with our pediatrician in May 2013, she observed Adrian and asked us questions about his behaviour, eating, and sleeping habits, and his development in general. As Adrian wasn't speaking, she advised that he undergo a private speech language assessment so that she could have a clearer picture of things. This assessment occurred shortly after our appointment on May 29, 2013. It is interesting to note that we decided to get Krisztian assessed as well, not because we had concerns about autism, but we were concerned that he wasn't talking at the level of an average child his age.

After the assessments were performed, the speech language pathologist sat with us to give us the results. With Krisztian, she explained that his receptive language abilities were within normal limits; however, his expressive language abilities were slightly delayed. This was something that we had anticipated, and all that was required was for him to attend additional speech and language sessions to improve in this area. We then discussed the results of Adrian's assessment. She proceeded to tell us the areas in which she had concerns. In her opinion, Adrian displayed limited eye contact and joint attention, he did not demonstrate any types of functional play, and he did not point or wave. Then, in a matter-of-fact yet professional manner, she looked at us and expressed that she had concerns of autism and recommended that Adrian undergo an autism assessment. She said that she would relay this information back to our pediatrician, and we would need to wait to hear back from her for follow-up.

When I sat in the car, the tears began to flow and I couldn't stop crying. This was the first time that any professional had said the word "autism." This word had run through my mind hundreds of times, but now that it had been said aloud, I felt that my fears about my son having autism could be a real possibility. It was all that I could think about, and the more I thought about it, the more I cried. The thought of my little boy living with this disorder was heartbreaking.

The following day, my pediatrician phoned me to inform me that she had shared the same concerns of autism as the speech language pathologist, and she strongly felt that Adrian should undergo an autism assessment. She told me that she had inquired into getting Adrian an appointment with the only private developmental pediatrician in the province at that time—however, this specialist was not accepting any new referrals. The only other option for Adrian was for him to be put on the wait-list at the Janeway, our local children's hospital, for a full-panel autism assessment. Then came even worse news: the wait-list for this assessment was twelve to eighteen months. I really couldn't believe what I was hearing.

I thought that I had misheard what she said, so I asked her, "I'm sorry, did you say twelve to eighteen months?" Yes, she said, this was indeed the time period, and it was the only available option at that time in the province. I then curtly replied, "Well, I guess I will be going out of province to get an assessment, because I refuse to wait that long for my child to get a diagnosis." At least with a diagnosis of autism, he could have access to government-funded applied behavioural analysis (ABA) therapy and other early intervention treatments. ABA therapy and other treatments could make major improvements to his life, but this could only happen if he had a diagnosis. It was nothing personal against our pediatrician—she just happened to be the bearer of bad news. While she was very understanding of our situation, there was simply nothing that she could do.

I felt completely hopeless, betrayed by our health care system, and I wondered why children would be denied timely services that would clearly be beneficial for their development. I couldn't believe that this was our only choice. I kept asking myself, "Is Newfoundland and Labrador truly a 'have' province if a child has to wait eighteen months to obtain a diagnosis for a major disability? What does this say about the true state of our health care system?" This situation didn't sit well with my husband or with me, and the fact that anybody would have to wait so long for any type of health care service in our province was simply unacceptable and, in our opinion, not reflective of sophisticated, westernized health care practices. Devoid of options in our own province, we began to look for alternatives elsewhere.

Two months later, Adrian was diagnosed with autism at a private clinic in Nova Scotia. It was devastating news to us, but at the same time, it was a relief finally to have a definitive answer to what was going on with our son. It had been a real struggle living with uncertainly for months. At least now that we were certain that Adrian had autism, we could focus our attention on getting him proper treatment.

The early days of trying to set up ABA therapy for Adrian were an arduous process. My husband and I were overwhelmed and still trying to process Adrian's diagnosis. In order to find a suitable therapist for him, we had to perform a litany of HR-related tasks such as placing an ad, setting up and performing interviews, hiring a successful applicant, and setting up banking information. These tasks were difficult, given our lack of expertise in these areas and our frame of mind at the time. We felt immense responsibility to hire the appropriate person, and this was difficult considering that there was a lack of precise criteria with respect to education or experience for the position. This is an area in which now, upon reflection, I wish there had been more support from the governmental health authority, Eastern Health, to help us and other parents in our situation. Luckily, we found a wonderful home therapist who fit well into our chaotic household and more importantly, is nurturing and takes great pride in working with Adrian and helping him reach his therapy goals.

Once our ABA therapy was put in place, I came to the realization that treating autism would be a multidisciplinary approach. My husband and I were, and still are, extremely satisfied with the superior quality of service that is being offered through the ABA program. However, we realized that different specialties would be required to treat areas outside of what the ABA program could offer. This is why the puzzle piece is such a perfect symbol for autism, as there is no "one size fits all" approach when it comes to treatment options. You have to know your child, and specialists have to get to know your child in order to ensure that he or she is working toward reasonable, attainable goals.

After Adrian was diagnosed, my life turned into a series of appointments. There were weekly speech language and occupational therapy appointments and senior therapist visits. There were also periodic appointments with Adrian's general pediatrician, developmental pediatrician, and family doctor. In addition to working, it became difficult to balance Adrian's appointments, keep up with the responsibilities of the household, and care for our other little boy and give him the proper love and attention that I felt he deserved. I often felt guilty for not having the extra time or energy to do things with Krisztian. I was somewhat realistic in that I knew I wasn't a superwoman and that I had to prioritize, but that doesn't mean it was easy to accept when things just couldn't get accomplished. Life itself was just overwhelming. I began to feel like the circus character frantically trying to keep spinning plates from crashing around me.

Adrian's diagnosis began to consume me, and it was beginning to manifest itself both emotionally and physically. This is when I came to the realization that it would be in our family's best interest for me to stay at home. If you asked the people who know me best if they ever thought I would be a stay-at-home mom, they would probably find the idea quite amusing. Admittedly, domesticity is not one of my greater skill sets. I am a terrible cook, and while I certainly take pride in my home, I am definitely not the Martha Stewart type. However, being a parent is the most selfless job in the world, and sometimes the job requires putting your family's interests before your own goals and aspirations. When Adrian was diagnosed with autism, I knew that I couldn't trust anybody else with the responsibility for his treatment. He was *my* child, and I felt that I owed him my devotion and determination to get him the best treatment options.

It's only when I became a stay-at-home mom that I came to have the greatest respect for what that job entails. Staying at home is definitely more difficult than working, as there are no scheduled breaks or vacation time, and time to oneself becomes a luxury of the past. Without a doubt, there are daily, often hourly challenges to staying home, but it's also gratifying in that I can focus my entire attention on my children. In particular, when it comes to Adrian's situation, staying at home allows me to take a more hands-on role in his treatment and have more input into the daily decisions of his treatment options.

In addition to having to pay out-of-pocket expenses for an autism diagnosis, some of the other obstacles that we have encountered have been with respect to getting additional therapy services that should be offered by our health care system. These additional services are essential to complement the ABA therapy that is being offered by the province. The Janeway Hospital's wait-lists for essential services such as speech language pathology and occupational therapy are inexcusable—and insulting—to parents who are trying to get the best treatment options for their children. The wait-lists for these services range from eighteen months to two years.

Once again, due to the deficiencies with our current health care system, I, along with many other parents, have had to resort to the use of private treatment options. Parents should not have to deal with this, and it is extremely unfair to many of our province's families who simply do not have the financial means to afford these types of services. On average, a private speech therapy session costs $60 for thirty minutes, and private occupational therapy costs approximately $125 per hour. What happens in most cases is that children end up paying the price. They are being denied services that can help them make the necessary developmental gains before they reach school age. This is also creating a two-tier health care system. Our system is supposed to be based on the premise that each individual has equal access to all health care services, irrespective of economic status.

Access to timely health care should not be based on ability to pay, but this is exactly what is happening to some children in our province who are diagnosed with autism. Due to unreasonable wait-lists, affluent families will access private services, while others will stay at the mercy of the timing of the public health care system. Even when a child gains access, most of the services are administered on a consultative basis, and follow-ups are done approximately every three months or on an as-needed basis. This is simply not enough support. More public health care positions need to be created to provide more autism support services. Again, I reiterate, aren't we a "have" province? If such positions cannot be provided publicly, then there needs to be increased provincial and federal funding for families to obtain these services privately, so that all individuals with autism can have equal treatment options.

It has been a little over a year since Adrian's diagnosis, and it has been, without a doubt, the most challenging year of my life. However, amazingly, it has made me a stronger person, and I've come to realize the things in my life that truly matter. Parents' love for their children is unconditional, and it is the purest type of love these children will ever find on this earth. The changes I have seen in Adrian within the last year are incredible. When I look back at reports from when he was first diagnosed, it amazes me how much progress he has made. His joint attention (where two individuals share focus on an object) and his eye contact have vastly improved. In terms of his receptive language, he understands ninety per cent of what I'm saying to him. While he isn't speaking yet, he is attempting vocalizations, and he has no problem letting me know when he does not like something. His attempts to communicate have also improved. He makes a vocalization and points at an item to indicate that he wants it. He waves bye-bye, claps his hands, dances, and demonstrates interests in a variety of ways.

He has also improved when it comes to playing with toys functionally. For instance, a year ago, he was obsessed with rocks. He could sit and examine them for hours. Trying to introduce a new toy or attempting to take him away from the rocks would upset him. Now he can play with a variety of items, such as blocks and picture games, and he takes turns playing educational games on the iPad.

Adrian's ability to partake in social activities has also improved. As an example, the difference from Halloween in 2013 to Halloween in 2014 was been remarkable. In 2013, we went around to a few cul-de-sacs with some similarly aged kids in the neighbourhood. We brought our sons around in a little red wagon, because at two years old they weren't able to walk for long periods of time. When the time came to knock on people's doors, Adrian refused to get out of the wagon, and he had a complete meltdown in the middle of the street. The only thing that would pacify him was examining rocks on the street. Of course, we wanted our other son to have an enjoyable Halloween experience, so my husband stayed with Adrian while I went around to a few houses with Krisztian. It's amazing, the difference with twins. Krisztian thought the whole Halloween experience was wonderful. He giggled when he knocked on people's doors, and a couple of times he just walked on into their homes to check them out. There was no inkling of shyness; he was just a little child enthralled with a new life experience. His brother, in contrast, was in a full plank position and screaming on the street. It certainly didn't make for a very successful first Halloween.

This year was very different. Adrian was compliant and enjoyed the whole experience. He didn't get upset, and he even knocked on the doors with his brother. At one point, he came upon some rocks and I held my breath, but he surprised me. He simply picked up a single rock and continued on. To most people this would be insignificant, but I was proud of the fact that he didn't get obsessed with the rocks, and I realized the amount of willpower that it took for him to do that. This year, by all definitions, Halloween was a success. It was a family activity that was enjoyed by all.

Even though Adrian has autism, I know it doesn't define him, and I fully love and support his individual interests and abilities and appreciate him for who he is. There are no limits to what a child with autism can do. Adrian reminds me of this every day. He has just turned three, and he can differentiate between shapes, all letters of the alphabet, and numbers one to twenty. He has also become much more aware of the world around him. He now notices when people leave or come to the house, he responds consistently to his name, and he gets upset when someone important to him goes away. There's also been an increase in his curiosity to explore and manipulate his physical environment. He used to be so cautious, but now he climbs on top of high tables and chairs, and opens cupboard doors to check out their contents. His comfort zone has expanded, and he is inquisitive to explore other parts of the house. This would never have happened a year ago. He is a very quick learner who is extremely focused and has an amazing memory. With most of his ABA programs, he only has to be shown a task once or twice and he completely understands what is expected of him.

As daunting as the diagnosis of autism is to parents, there is nothing more gratifying than seeing your child overcome challenges and make progress. It makes you feel more accepting of the diagnosis, and it gives you the belief that your child and other children with this disorder can grow up and have fulfilling lives. Adrian now attends part-time daycare two mornings a week, and swimming and Kindermusik once a week. He is a happy, even-tempered little boy who can now adapt well to new situations.

There are still everyday challenges, but with a lot of hard work, love, and faith, these challenges have become more manageable. This has mainly become possible through advocacy, and this is the best piece of advice that I would like to give to parents—do not be afraid to speak out for your child. Obtaining autism services is an intimidating process. There are many services in the province, but the information is not always easy to find. As a parent, you have to put yourself out there and go beyond your comfort zone. I cannot recall how many times I called the Child Development Centre at the Janeway Hospital to see where Adrian was on the wait-list for various services. You have to be an advocate. No one is more invested in your child's well-being than you, and unfortunately you will be the one having to do most of the work to seek out the services.

Additionally, I have found networking with other parents to be beneficial. It's helpful to talk to others who understand the challenges and obstacles of autism, and they are also great sources of information. For me, knowledge is power, and the more knowledge I have about new advances in autism research or services, the more it benefits my son. Lastly, I strongly feel it is important not to compare a child with autism to other children. Before Adrian was diagnosed, I always compared him to other children, and I often felt disheartened that he was not at the same developmental level. Eventually, I realized that this was futile, and that it was more important for me to focus on Adrian's strengths and his progress. As I began to focus on his progress, I began to take pride in his individuality. Once I was able to take this leap, I was able to focus more on the similarities rather than the differences between him and other children.

Almost a year to the day after Adrian's diagnosis, I had the opportunity to attend a Jon Bon Jovi private acoustic concert and have my picture taken with him. Jon Bon Jovi is an artist I greatly respect, and he was recently honoured with the Marian Anderson Award. This award is given to an artist who uses his celebrity to benefit humanity as a whole. In his acceptance speech, he was extremely humble, but one of his comments really resonated with me. He spoke of "the shared belief in the basic dignity of the human soul, and how with a little bit of hope and opportunity, people from all walks of life have the potential to aspire to greatness and, along the way, inspire others." My children are my greatest inspiration, and they both inspire me daily to be a better mother, wife, and person as a whole. With autism, so much hinges on hope, as there is so much about the disorder that is uncertain. I have so much hope for both of my children, and particularly for Adrian—with a little hope and opportunity, he will be able to meet his potential and aspire to his own level of greatness.

In 2013, Katrina Bajzak decided to suspend her professional activities to devote herself full-time to her two sons, especially to advocate and to coordinate therapeutic services and activities for her son Adrian. Katrina is involved in the autism community and is a strong advocate for reducing the current wait-list times for children in Newfoundland and Labrador to obtain an autism diagnosis.

Embracing the Not Normal

by Jessica Butt

Jessica Butt was born in St. Catharine's, Ontario, in 1982. At a young age she relocated with her family to the east coast of Canada and now resides in the village of Eastern Passage, Nova Scotia. After graduating high school, Jessica ran a small but thriving dance studio until the birth of her first child.

The scariest part about autism spectrum disorder is the misconception of the disease. When we think about autism, we picture severely disadvantaged kids, who have little to no capacity for human interaction—humming to themselves, never making eye contact, happy to exist in their own private world. At least, that's what I believed autism to be, before I came to know it first-hand.

It was November 2011, just after his seventh birthday, when the doctors determined that my son Harrison did in fact have autism spectrum disorder. The road to diagnosis, however, began much earlier.

When Harrison was four years old, we decided to put him in a part-time preschool program. We wanted him to spend time with other children his own age, to learn some necessary skills for school. After all, he was an only child and surrounded daily by adults.

Arriving one morning at pickup time, I came across my child, sitting alone in a small chair outside the classroom door. "What are you doing out here?" I asked. "I was disturbing the mat," he replied. It seemed that during reading time, a daily activity at preschool, Harrison had expressed his distaste for the particular story being shared. When he wouldn't be silenced, they moved him to the corridor for quiet reflection. "Were you sad, sitting all by yourself out here?" I asked, and his reply was simple and honest. "No. It was quiet in the hallway, and I didn't want to listen to that story anyways!"

It was brought to our attention very early that our child stood out from the rest. "They think he might be autistic," I explained during a Thanksgiving dinner at my in-laws' home. "Isn't that the most ridiculous thing you've ever heard?" I continued. Sitting across the table from me, trying desperately to avoid my gaze, was Cathy, a very close family friend and one of the most genuine, no-nonsense women I know. "Do you think he could have autism?" I asked her directly. Though she hesitated for only a moment, I knew the answer before she even opened her mouth to speak. It was her opinion that Harrison displayed several common characteristics of autism. The hand flapping was one of the most obvious.

Looking back, it's hard to pinpoint when the hand flapping began. It seems like a part of him that was always there. He would get so excited, over a new toy or while watching his favourite show, that he simply could not sit still. He would move from one foot to the other while his hands danced near his ears. It was clear to us that Harrison displayed a few unusual behaviours. Having said that, he was our first child, the first grandchild, the sun rose and set on his sweet face, and though we knew he had a few eccentricities, we loved him all the more for it.

As a child, Harrison was singularly focused. If it didn't have wheels or an engine, he wasn't interested. In hindsight, it's easy to say that we should have noticed this was odd, but we just thought he was a typical little boy, obsessed with diggers and backhoes, trucks and trains, dirt and sand. I can see him standing in the dining room, just the right height so that his nose practically rested on the tabletop. He would line up his trains and drive them slowly by his face, taking special care to look closely at each car as it passed. As he grew, his interests never broadened. There were no superheroes, or imaginative play, just his trusty cars and trucks.

If you had asked me ten years ago to name the most boring sport known to man, it would have been easy to answer. Back then, I wouldn't have even classified NASCAR as a sport. Grown men driving in circles for hours? Come on. Now my life is filled with facts and knowledge about the sport that has captivated my son's heart. Not only can I name more than twenty drivers, I know more information and statistics than I ever thought possible. Watching the Daytona 500—from start to finish, I might add—is now commonplace for me. We even check race standings in the newspaper over Froot Loops at the breakfast table. One of the exceptional things about Harrison is his ability to obtain and maintain information. If he hears or reads something of interest to him, it never leaves.

Harrison's love of all things to do with racing is second only to his love of music. He has the uncanny ability to hear a song once and be able not only to name the artist or track, but to sing it for you. At an early age he showed a fascination for music, especially the guitar, and though he was desperate to play one, his hands were still far too small. It was at this point that someone suggested the ukulele—much smaller and a perfect fit. It even looked like a little guitar. He was hooked, so we took lessons at a nearby music studio. After a year of ukulele, we switched to the acoustic guitar, and finally last year to a Blue Fernandes Stratocaster; one step closer to his dream of being like front man Billie Joe Armstrong, of Green Day fame. Together with his exceptional teacher, Harrison has far exceeded our expectations, and though—like most parents, I'm sure—we'd like him to practise more, it is clear that he has a natural talent.

To say that school has been a struggle would be a gross understatement. Though the idea that something was different about Harrison had already been planted by his preschool teachers, we weren't willing to believe that his behaviour was real cause for concern. He lacked self-help skills. He couldn't fasten his own coat or put on his school bag at the end of the day. "He's a boy," my mom would say. Boys are always less independent and, for lack of a better word, lazier than girls. After all, how would he know those skills when they were never expected of him? We always dressed and prepped him for the day. I remember asking Harrison what he did while all the other children got ready to go outside for recess. "Why don't you try to put your coat and boots on yourself?" I asked. His answer was simple: "My friend Sydney does it for me." In the short time he had been going to school, he had already found a motherly replacement, in the form of a kind little girl who knew he needed her help.

At least twice a week his teacher would take me aside at day's end to discuss Harrison's shortcomings. He doesn't work independently. He can't maintain focus to finish a task. It was clear that this teacher was frustrated by Harrison and the extra challenges he presented in her classroom daily. It was in that first year of school that I discovered how quickly some teachers search for a label. There must be something wrong with him, was the implied messaged.

"He's a late bloomer." This was the common response from friends and loved ones. "He does things at his own pace. He'll get there, just give him time." It seemed accurate. By the middle of kindergarten he had shown a great deal of improvement. He was settling into a routine and was growing more familiar with what was expected of him. You would think that this would be a time to praise his success, no matter how small. Unfortunately, this was not the case. Instead of acknowledging how far this little boy had come, a new set of problems were presented. "He lacks empathy. He lives in his own little world, and doesn't seem affected by those around him. He has no filter, and often his words are hurtful to the other children." I became frustrated and miserable, dreading the numerous discussions, with no help or suggestions from the school, just more problems being brought to my attention.

In second grade, something wonderful happened, and school changed for the better. Her name was Mrs. Gallant, and she was sent from heaven to show us what a teacher is supposed to be, to show us what kindness and support could look like, and to connect with our child on a deeper level. Mrs. Gallant opened my eyes to many things I had never noticed about my own child. "Do you know he never makes eye contact?" she observed one day after school. "Of course he does," I said. "He looks right at me whenever we talk." To which she replied, "He loves you." I had taken for granted that the person he was at home was the same person that the rest of the world got to see.

After a few months of parent-teacher conferences, discussing Harrison's accomplishments and his areas of concern, and putting in place tools to help him with his daily routine, it was finally time for our appointment with the autism team. After an entire morning of questions and assessments, the doctor concluded that our seven-year-old had autism spectrum disorder. That wasn't the first, and certainly not the last time I shed tears for my boy. But Dr. Shea said something to me that I will never forget. "You're leaving here today with the same boy you came with. This diagnosis doesn't change who he is, or who he is to you." When I shared the news with Mrs. Gallant, we cried together.

As Harrison grew, we began to notice changes and new difficulties. While he had never been the best eater—"Eeww, vegetables!"—he had enjoyed a variety of foods. With age, however, his eating habits changed dramatically. He has a handful of foods that he is willing to entertain, and a fierce reluctance to try anything new.

With age also came strange anxiety, worry, and fear over things that shouldn't be troubling, such as a car driving in circles in the parking garage, or a song playing on repeat. In the beginning, we just managed these anxieties and outbursts as best we could, but it became clear that we were ill-equipped.

In May of 2011, just months before the official diagnosis, we took a family vacation to Bethel, Maine. After arriving and settling in for a few days, we decided to take a day trip to explore our surroundings. We programmed the GPS and set out on our way. Unexpectedly, we came upon construction. No problem, we turned right instead of left and followed the signs for the detour. After a few moments, it became clear that we had arrived back at our original position. "Recalculating," came the familiar cry of the ever-so-helpful GPS lady. "Maybe we missed a sign in the detour," said Daddy, already seeing the trepidation in Harrison's face. "We'll just try again."

And try again we did, to no avail. The only way to describe what happened next is a total collapse, a meltdown if you will. Tears spilled down his face, and his cries were urgent. "Why are we driving in circles? Why does the GPS keep telling us the wrong way? Please . . . I just want to go home. Why can't we just go home?" It seemed hopeless. The more we tried to calm and soothe, the louder and angrier he became. It was the most intense and unmanageable moment my memory can recall, and although I'd like to be able to offer the perfect solution, I can't. The truth is, these moments of severe anxiety leave me with anxiety of my own. His breakdown often leads to my breakdown.

In the early winter of 2012, we were offered an opportunity that would help us tremendously. The Izaak Walton Killam Children's Hospital was holding a support group for parents and children who suffered with autism-related anxiety. The meetings were held twice a week, for a twelve-week period. We were anxious, but excited to learn strategies for coping, and to connect with other children and families living with autism. Sometimes, just being able to compare notes with another person can ease the difficulties that we often feel we are facing alone.

The progress was slow, but evident. We were learning to identify his fears, and triggers. By determining which fears were "false alarms," we could use several strategies to overcome the anxiety. We began every session with a deep breathing exercise that the children took turns leading. Once we identified Harrison's main fears—in his case, repeating songs, trying new foods, and getting lost—we used the stepladder system. We broke down the fear into a series of simple steps that we could use to work up to confronting the fear. For example, with new food, the stepladder would be as follows:

Step One: Smell the food.
Step Two: Put the food to your lips.
Step Three: Put the food in your mouth, then take it back out.
Step Four: Take a small bite of food.
Step Five: Take a bite of food and swallow.

We would work on each step until we felt comfortable moving to the next one. By the end of the twelve weeks, Harrison had overcome several of his smaller fears and was making real progress with the bigger ones. Don't get me wrong, these issues have never left us. New foods are still a challenge, and getting lost is still a source of concern, but now we can use the tools we learned to calm the anxiety. If we get lost, we can ask someone for directions. If he eats broccoli and hates it, the world won't stop turning, he just won't eat broccoli again. For someone like Harrison, these rationalizations were very valuable.

Harrison has always been a child of logic. In his world, things are black or white. Often there is no grey. If you ask his opinion, he will share it, and it won't be sugar-coated or have a rosy glow. The truth, for him, is all there is. A perfect example of this was the discussion of Groundhog Day. We all know the tradition. If the groundhog sees his shadow, he will retreat to his burrow, and winter will persist for six more weeks. Harrison's reaction was, "That's ridiculous. The first day of spring is March 21, so whether the groundhog sees his shadow or not, there WILL be six more weeks of winter. It's science."

While we often acknowledge the mental and emotional difficulties people affected by autism endure, there are also many physical obstacles to overcome. As an infant, Harrison was bright and alert.

He was sleeping through the night at only eight weeks and began speaking at eleven months. He would sit with his toys, content to play for hours. Harrison didn't crawl until twelve months, and he wasn't walking until he had almost reached his second birthday. It seemed he lacked the curiosity that often encourages children to explore.

As he got older, the physical barriers continued to appear. Harrison was incredibly clumsy and often fell over himself. He never alternated feet while going up and down stairs, but most importantly, he only ever seemed to walk on the balls of his feet. Though he enjoys watching and learning about many sports, his difficulty with large motor skills impedes him, thus making sports exceedingly difficult. His experiences with soccer, while positive from a social aspect, were proof that competitive sports of any kind were not in the cards. He was happier to observe the comings and goings of the other players rather than get in on the action himself. I think in three summer seasons of soccer, I could count on one hand the number of times I saw him make contact with the ball.

During one summer vacation, we took a special trip with some friends to Upper Clements Park, a local attraction with rides and waterslides and a petting zoo. All of the children were eager to reach their preferred ride, and Harrison was no exception. Not one for Ferris wheels or the merry-go-round (because the merry-go-round plays the same song on repeat), his choice was simple: the go-karts. But not your average go-karts, since he hadn't actually been brave enough to try those yet, with the noise and the continuous circles, but pedal go-karts. We made our way over and waited impatiently for our turn. Now, I should mention that our success with bike riding up to this point was non-existent. The few times we had taken Harrison out to ride the bike he got for Christmas always ended in disaster. He would become frustrated, and we would become frustrated, and the event would usually end in tears. But I was optimistic that day. He was a little older, and clearly excited, and feeling confident about riding the karts himself. Soon his turn came, and clad in his helmet and strapped in, he started out.

It was obvious after only moments that his endeavour would not be a happy one. Though he tried desperately to push his legs and manoeuvre the pedals, he wasn't moving. The situation was made worse by the large crowd of people, waiting for their turns, watching the scene unfold. Hushed whispers and judgment filled the air, and soon tears began to fall. Not just his, but mine, too. "I can't do it," he called to me, and while I wanted to cheer him on and tell him he could, I knew it wasn't that simple. The bright spot in this dark moment was that it led us to take action. The IWK Children's Hospital has an exceptional recreational therapy program. We were able to borrow a specialized bicycle with wider wheels for stability, and Harrison could ride a bike and be proud of his accomplishment.

In May of 2014, my sister-in-law, Keliegh, presented us with an incredible opportunity to contribute our story to this book. We spoke candidly on speakerphone in Harrison's presence. Up to this point we hadn't officially told Harrison about his diagnosis. We knew the time would come, but we wanted to wait. We figured he was blissfully unaware, and leading a perfectly productive life. He knew he had challenges, but we were working on them together. When the conversation ended, I said, "Isn't this exciting?" To which Harrison replied, "I'm going to be in a book? I'll be famous!"

We all had a little chuckle, and then his mood shifted. Quietly he said, "I didn't know I had autism." To say that it's difficult to explain a condition such as autism to your child, when you yourself have only a very basic knowledge of it, would be a gross understatement. Here's what we came up with. While autism affects him in negative ways, from his difficulty with printing and cutting to his clumsiness and ineptitude for sports, it is also a blessing, giving him a superior ability to learn and retain information, an uncanny knack for observation, and a hilarious and gentle nature. Autism has given us a child who is exceptional.

Later, while driving across the MacDonald Bridge on our way to Halifax, he asked, "So, I'm not normal?" To which I replied, "Who wants to be normal?" And I couldn't have been more serious. Everyone has something that sets them apart from the crowd—irrational fears, unexpected talents. It's the not normal that keeps things interesting.

So my advice to other parents living with autism is simple. Every day is made up of moments of happiness and laughter at unexpected times, of sorrow and unpredictable sadness, accomplishments and frustrations big and small. Take the time to acknowledge each moment, and embrace the not normal.

Jessica Butt is now a part of her family's accounting firm. She is happily married to her high school sweetheart and the proud mother of three remarkable children. Along with her love of all things creative, Jessica also has a taste for travel and adventure.

Life Changer

by Krista Preuss-Goodreault

Krista Preuss-Goudreault was born in Brantford, Ontario, in the late 1960s. After high school, she earned an honours degree in French language and literature from Wilfrid Laurier University and a Bachelor of Education degree at the University of Western Ontario. She taught French for several years in local elementary schools, but she felt a strong pull back to the private sector to help with the expansion of her family business. It was there that Krista met her husband, Joe, and the couple were married in 1998. Krista and Joe have three children: Olivia, Emily, and Matthew. Olivia, their oldest daughter, was diagnosed with autism (specifically Asperger's syndrome) in 2010.

When my daughter Olivia was ten years old, and after many doctors' appointments with specialists such as a psychologist, a neurologist, and a psychiatrist, the results were in. "Asperger's syndrome," they called it, the highest-functioning part of the autism spectrum.

I remember crying a little when they told us, but I think it was just from sheer relief. After years of disapproving glares at the grocery store when Olivia melted down into a screaming puddle, to my daily meetings with Olivia's teachers where they outlined her shortcomings and troubling behaviours (that in *all* of their collective years of teaching they had never come across), to my feelings of continually failing as a mother, I wondered what was wrong with my child. I was a crumbling mess of emotion on a daily basis. But now, it finally all made sense. And it even had a name.

I remember Olivia looking at me, alarmed at my tears. She said, "What? Am I dying of a deadly disease?" I pulled myself together long enough to say, "No, honey, you have Asperger's syndrome. It's going to be okay."

Right away I began my quest to find a book to explain ASD to a ten-year-old girl. She needed to understand that she didn't have a deadly disease and, mostly, that she wasn't alone. I remember looking for a kid's book, but I just couldn't find one that was simple enough for her to grasp, so my daughter and I decided to write our own.

Olivia and I talked about what it was like to be a kid on the spectrum, and I wrote down what she said. She told me things I had never heard her say before, and I was amazed at her eloquence and insight as she discussed her own perspectives. Somehow, it had never occurred to me who it was that I should be asking about what it was like to have Asperger's syndrome. Who was the actual expert here? To be awarded this rare look into her mind was like a precious gift, and it was only then that my mind began to shift and to see things through her eyes. It was a godsend, really. She was different. She wasn't wrong or bad or broken—she was awesome!

We finished our little book, and there it sat, on the dining room table, gathering dust while life went on around it. Olivia's diagnosis, although a relief of sorts, didn't change her. She was the same girl the day before her diagnosis and the day after, and we loved her just the same.

It wasn't until a couple of years ago that I decided to self-publish our book. It was going to be for Olivia's birthday, just for her and for our close friends and family. I had no grandiose plans for becoming a famous author. Frankly, I'm not a writer in real life. I just had a story to tell.

When it was in print, I nervously offered up our prized possession to the local bookstore owner, almost wincing for fear that it wasn't really all that good and that perhaps I should have worked on it harder and longer to make it better, but knowing that this little book changed something inside of me and that maybe it could change someone else, too.

"This book needs to be in every school, doctor's office, and library, my dear," the bookstore owner said. And there it began . . .

Liv did her first book reading there at this store, and we packed the place. Our little book has now travelled the globe and has reached Australia, Italy, the UK, India, and even Costa Rica! It turns out, people want to know about autism and its various forms. It touches all of us.

Olivia now travels around our region doing readings at bookstores and schools and many different venues and events. She also has a speech about what it's like to be a kid with Asperger's syndrome. To be honest, she was born for the stage. It's almost like watching a butterfly gaining its wings and soaring off with a beauty that is unknown even to them.

Tucking her surly, teenaged attitude in her back pocket, Olivia flawlessly rises to the occasion and speaks with the trained finesse of a public speaker. She is articulate and funny, and I feel so proud I could burst as I watch her in her element, being Olivia.

The book and her speaking engagements have done wonders for Olivia's self-esteem, and she looks forward to each and every event. Because she needs lots of time to transition, I am always careful to ask her if she would like to participate, and with as much notice as possible, so that Olivia can mentally prepare herself. We will only continue to attend events and speak about Asperger's if it is her choice. She is the star of our events, and I am her wingman. That's my role, and it suits me just fine.

What Olivia doesn't know, though, is that, as her mom, I tear up every time I hear her speak because I am so proud of my Aspie girl. She doesn't know about the nights I would lie awake wondering why God gave her to me, or why she couldn't be just like every other kid, or why she melted down over seemingly nothing while other parents looked on disapprovingly, or why at birthday parties she wouldn't participate in the party games but would be found, off in her own little world, away from the noise, picking dandelions or rocks, or why the teachers would call me to say that she refused to go into the gym because she said it was too loud or that she appeared hysterical when the fire alarm sounded or that she would sit underneath her desk for long periods because the classroom seemed so overwhelming.

My daughter, Olivia Goodreault.

She didn't know that the teachers said that I shouldn't be sitting with her to do her homework because she was perfectly capable. "She's such a smart girl, we can't understand . . . perhaps she might just need a time out or two for poor behaviour." Oh, how that broke my heart.

What Olivia doesn't know, as I watch her tell her story, is how I felt like the worst mother in Canada, and cried often to my own mother about why she didn't seem to recognize my facial expressions or why she endlessly studied and touched the carpet fibres on our living room floor as a toddler instead of playing with her toys. My own mother had no answers.

And lastly, what Olivia doesn't know is that writing our little book was a catharsis for me in the truest sense of the word. It helped me, as she talked to me, those days when we worked on our book. When she was articulating all that she did, it suddenly dawned on me that I was trying to change her, too, to fit into my own mould of what my child should be like. Instead, I needed to accept her differences, because that's all they are—differences, not deficits—and they are to be celebrated! Suddenly, I stopped being afraid of the disapproving looks and the lists of her so-called deficiencies at school and the gossiping mothers. I realized that I was too wrapped up in other people's expectations. Olivia herself helped me to finally realize that I love her, whoever she is, and when you dance to the beat of your own drum, that is a truly amazing and courageous and admirable gift. She won't ever be confined to a box, like so many of us, and that is what freedom looks like.

Acceptance can really change who you are. I am living proof. And when you learn a lesson from a child, it's a mighty important one. For me, it was a life changer.

I learned all of this from my ten-year-old kid with Asperger's syndrome . . . that, and how to pick the most beautiful dandelions and the sparkliest rocks.

In 2011, Krista Preuss-Goodreault and her daughter Olivia co-authored a children's book about what it's like to be a kid with autism, entitled May I Be Excused, My Brain is Full. *Since then, their book has travelled around the globe, and the pair have travelled across the country to tell their story and to empower other kids with autism to take pride in who they are. Olivia was invited to read her book and to speak at the National Asperger's Conference in Winnipeg in 2013 and most recently has spoken to a first-year class at York University, explaining what it's like to have Asperger's syndrome. Krista is passionate about autism awareness and speaks candidly to many groups about being a mother to a child with special needs. She has a thriving Facebook page named for the book's title, and she is beginning work on a second book, about Olivia's transition to high school.*

"I Don't Have a Disability, I Have a Special Ability"

by Dawn Haire-Butt

After receiving a breast cancer diagnosis in 2006, Dawn Haire-Butt gave up her accounting career to become a stay-at-home mom. It was the most difficult time of her life, but it would become a blessing in disguise. Two years later, her son Kyle was diagnosed with autism. Here was another battle that would require a strong will and an I-will-not-take-no-for-an-answer attitude.

At eighteen months old, Kyle picked up a picture of an eggplant and said, "Purple." He didn't play with toy cars, or wrestlers, or want to hang out with the neighbourhood kids. He wanted books, Legos, science kits, and informational movies. We would take him to the mall and he would "disappear." Boy, was he quick. Everyone would be frantic trying to locate him, and usually we would find him curled up with a book or in the movie section. Kyle had Walmart calling a Code Adam at least once a week.

Beginning school was both a chore and a blessing for Kyle. The social interactions, the noises, assemblies, lunchtimes—so much going on, and he didn't know how to handle it. On the other hand, there was a library, with so many books and so much information to read. He could memorize anything, but printing his own name was a chore. Playing with other children was very foreign. He would stand off by himself but mimic other kids. At his kindergarten graduation, all the children got up to introduce themselves and tell what they wanted to be when they grew up. When it was Kyle's turn, he got up and introduced himself, then said, "When I grow up I want to be a paleontologist." Most parents didn't know what it was, let alone how to spell it. When everyone started to chuckle, Kyle came back to the mic and said, "Stop laughing at me, stop laughing at me." He didn't understand that they weren't making fun of him. Remember, Kyle wasn't diagnosed until grade two, so my husband and I and the teachers were all doing our best to find out the solution to what was going on with our son.

Kyle was still at the top of his class academically, but socially, I was noticing that he was behind. He would run and hide when he was hurt, afraid, frustrated, or when something caught his attention. Kyle could be right next to you as you were calling him, but he would be so engrossed or afraid, he wouldn't answer. He had a voracious appetite for reading and would always have a book under his arm wherever he went. At times the teacher would have to take his book so he could participate in class. Even now, in grade eight, Kyle has to be told to put the book away by his teacher. Books are Kyle's way to handle the world, his way to de-stimulate and relax, to rid himself of the stresses of the day.

We also took note of his fixations. In his younger years, it was dinosaurs. He devoured anything to do with dinosaurs and could tell you the most trivial facts about them. He was obsessed with the movie *The Land Before Time* and had to have three copies of the movie replaced because he watched it so often.

Then he moved from dinosaurs into animals in general. At Kyle's primary school, if a teacher or anyone had a question about animals, Kyle was their point of reference. When something caught his attention, he needed to know anything and everything about it. It was when he was in grade one that I really started to ask myself and everyone else questions about Kyle and his unusual behaviour. After speaking with his teacher, the guidance counsellor, and the principal, we decided to monitor Kyle and see where it would take us. Christmas of that year, Kyle's older sister (my stepdaughter) came for a visit. Jaimee, who already had a younger brother diagnosed as autistic, was aware of the problems we were encountering with Kyle. Her comment was, "Dawn, Kyle reminds me so much of Evan with his actions. Do you think he could be autistic?" She started to fill me in on her brother and his behaviours. When school opened I spoke to the teacher, guidance counsellor, principal, and the instructional resource teachers (IRTs), and we were all in agreement that this was something we should check into.

I didn't want to waste any time, so we put a plan in place. The guidance counsellor would begin filling out paperwork required by the school board, and we would put in place any supports we could. I started with our family doctor and had a referral sent to Child Development at the Janeway Children's Hospital. I called Child Development, and the referral was sent to get some understanding about how this would be handled. I was told that it would take eighteen months to two years—that was unacceptable! He would have another two years of school with no help. So my next step was to go to the Autism Society, Newfoundland and Labrador to see if they could shed some light on the situation, to find out about autism, and to see if anyone would put Kyle into that category. I wanted to talk to someone who dealt with this on a daily basis and find out what the setbacks would be of a delayed diagnosis.

I began phoning Child Development on a weekly basis, to get information, names, and numbers, to find out who does what, who to talk to, what was the process, and most importantly, when Kyle would get his appointment.

As we ended the grade one school year, we still had no answers for Kyle. I thought, *Enough is enough*. I called everyone on the school board, from the chief executive officer (CEO) and senior education officer (SEO) to the program specialists, you name it. I was still calling Child Development weekly, hoping for a breakthrough. By then I was starting with the hospital hierarchy, then on to the provincial government's Department of Education and Department of Health. Next I decided to call my Member of the House of Assembly (MHA). After I spoke with him and his assistant, explaining my frustrations and showing them my mounds of paperwork, research, names, and numbers, they decided to try to help me get Kyle seen by a specialist at least. By now, of course, everyone in Eastern Health knew my name and what I was pushing for. Within ten days, the intake secretary from the Janeway called me with an appointment with Dr. Kathy Vardy. Finally!

After a few hours with Dr. Vardy, the results were confirmed. Kyle was autistic—more specifically, he had Asperger's syndrome. I was given a lot of information, but we still needed an assessment. Now came another bombshell—it could take up to a year, maybe longer. What? This was not happening! Dr. Vardy did agree to notify the principal and guidance counsellor in writing of her diagnosis, to help with school in September, but we still needed the assessment. I called our MHA back and filled him in on our appointment and the new wait-list. I thought to myself, *We're halfway through July. Kyle is not going to school without all the help he needs.* I got up one morning and decided to call the premier's office. I got his executive assistant on the phone and explained my dilemma. I cried, danced, yelled, and threatened to camp out in the foyer with the media if Kyle wasn't assessed. I was called the next day with an appointment for an assessment within a week.

This time I went in ready for another battle! We spent the day at the Janeway and it was confirmed, Kyle was autistic. I was told about his strengths, his weaknesses, what we should concentrate on, how to handle situations. Appointments were made with occupational therapists, physiotherapists, speech therapists, you name it. All of a sudden, things were moving so quickly. We were one step ahead because, before leaving school in June, we had everything set up in the event I managed to fight my way through. Dr. Vardy had already sent her report to the school and the committee would fast-track their report, as there was less than a month left before school started. I went into this assessment like a woman of steel, ready to take on the world, and I left a blubbering mess.

Before ending our appointment, Dr. Vardy, along with two or three of her colleagues, said to me, "Dawn, Kyle is going to do just fine. He is an amazing child, well-established, very well-behaved, knows his limits, and looks up to his mother like no other child I've ever seen in here. We pushed him to his limit today, and other than a few choice words, there was never a meltdown. He knows how to self-soothe, he does the breathing techniques, and you can see him think before he reacts. He has come this far without a diagnosis due to you, the positive way you are raising him, and the time and effort you put into parenting. Now that he has his diagnosis and will have all the help and support that is here for him, I can see him doing wonderful things in life, and it will be because he has you by his side."

Not only had I worried that while I was waiting for a diagnosis I might be doing something that could harm my child's progress, I had just finished up breast cancer treatment. I had discovered a lump I would never have found if Kyle hadn't jumped on me one day in kindergarten. The doctors and nurses didn't realize just how poignant their words to me were. Not only was I saving Kyle's life, but he had also saved mine.

After diagnosis, we started to notice all the things that were there before for which we had no explanation. Loud noises would send Kyle running around with his hands over his ears. Now I knew why. He still has the same sensitivity. Once he was in elementary school, we also noticed that Kyle had some phobias, specifically about clowns and Egyptian mummies. When he was little, a show would come on TV and Kyle would run from the room screaming if it had Egyptian mummies in it. Now here we were, seven years later, battle swords lowered a little but ready to fight if need be.

Kyle is thriving in grade eight, still with his idiosyncrasies but doing amazingly well. He has two good friends, Emily and Derrick. Derrick has been his best friend since kindergarten and has always been there for him, even when they had their own issues. Emily is his "best friend that is a girl" and she brings out the best in him. She is his confidant, his date, the person he can "be Kyle" with. Then there's his family: his ten-year-old sister, Emily, is making sure he keeps up on the social aspects and teaching him social skills that he otherwise wouldn't have. She needles him when she needs to and defends him when she needs to do that. Dad's job is to hang out in the shed and teach him "man" things, have "man" talks, and show him how to let things "roll off his back." Mom is there for, well, everything.

The doctors' words were truer than they thought. I have had metastases, but I've had clear reports for over a year now. So I'm here for the good, the bad, and the battles that all four of us will wage, if Kyle needs us to.

From Kyle's diagnosis on, I can honestly say that, regarding his education, Kyle has met any obstacles efficiently and quickly. The school is always one hundred per cent behind me with Kyle and provides any supports he may need. In meetings with intensive support programmers, they take my ideas and thoughts seriously, as I do theirs. Medically, Kyle has had all the supports he has needed over the past years and still does. If I have questions about Kyle, or notice something I find odd, many times my calls are picked up right away or returned very promptly. Sometimes a quick visit is required. Any time another specialist's opinion is needed, it is always handled very efficiently.

Kyle still visits with an autism specialist once a year, just to touch base, and to make sure we are still on a good path and things are going fine. Aside from the first year fighting to get him diagnosed, I can honestly say that my experience with autism and Kyle has been a wonderful, eye-opening one to date. It's been a learning experience for everyone in our family and a fabulous journey when we have taken the time to watch with awe his amazing exception-ality. The depth of his knowledge and amount of information that his brain can retain is astonishing. I watched the Temple Grandin documentary with Kyle. They flashed pictures on the screen to show the way she remembers so much information. I looked at my son and said, "Kyle, is that how you remember?" His response was, "Mom, isn't that how everyone remembers?" How little we really know! Kyle has never been on any kind of medication, and he has progressed so much since his diagnosis. When you have the information and tools you need, you can accomplish anything.

We have had some challenges over the years, and I expect we will always have challenges. I say "we" because, when Kyle has a challenge, our whole family pitches in to help overcome or deal with it. Speech is still somewhat of an issue for Kyle; with "R" and "W" he reverts to baby talk, and he speaks in a monotone. Kyle has always had a monotonous, unemotional speech pattern. I always warn anyone who wants to pick Kyle's brain, "If you ask, be prepared for a well-informed answer." Until Kyle begins, no one truly understands how much information is stored away in his file bank.

Kyle has learned to add emotion to his speech somewhat, and socially he is doing much better. He's getting double meanings, and he understands that there is more to comprehension than just black and white. In the past year he has discovered comedy, and he is starting to be able to really distinguish between fun-making and fun-fun. There are still some issues, but we will deal with those as they arise. Lineups still cause Kyle some stress, but not as much as they did when he was younger. Our big success is with running. Kyle no longer hides, runs, or takes off. He is learning to deal with his feelings, to ask for help, and to talk about what is bothering him.

His phobias about mummies and clowns are still there. Mummies are becoming a little less intimidating as time goes on, but clowns are really hard for him to deal with. They still leave him shaking and feeling frustrated. If Kyle is going to have a meltdown, a clown is probably what will do it. I'm sure loud noises will also always be a challenge. His hearing is sensitive to sounds, which to him are sometimes very painful.

Things didn't just get better on their own; it took a lot of work, different techniques, a change of attitude, and as much support as we could get. Some of the best things I have ever done to help Kyle, without knowing he was autistic, was to set rules and guidelines and to teach him that every action has a reaction. I've always believed in having a calm household with no yelling or aggression. I encourage my children to talk to each other, be honest, not to be ashamed of how they feel, to give hugs, and—our big one—to tell each other "I love you" every day.

Autism didn't give Kyle a pass: he still had to go by our household rules. One of the things we have done is to give Kyle his own space. Kyle's bedroom is Kyle's. You have to knock and wait for Kyle to answer before going in, though there is a time limit for Mom and Dad. He gets to pick out the colours, design, and bedding for his room. The same goes for his toy room, or reading room. When Kyle is anxious or frustrated, we start out by sitting down and holding hands while breathing slowly in and out and counting to ten. Even now, in grade eight, Kyle will stop and do his breathing exercises.

We have our very own "autism hug." When Kyle is overstimulated, he bangs himself off either side of the hallway while walking to his bedroom. I automatically know he has had a rough day, so I go in the room and say, "Autism hug?" "Yes, please, Mom." I put both my arms around him until my hands are clasped, he puts his arms around my neck and lays his head on my shoulder, and I squeeze as hard as I can. And we just hug like that for five or ten minutes. His little sister, Emily, also asks for "autism hugs" because they look like so much fun. Before going to bed at night, we have a chit-chat and talk about the day, how it went, and how he feels, and before school each day I give Kyle a pep talk. I might say, "Have a good day, good luck on your test, you know you're amazing." Then we run over what is happening throughout the day in point-by-point form. Everyone has ideas and techniques that work for them and their families. These are ours.

School hasn't really been an issue for Kyle since his diagnosis. Of course, he has had his challenges with other students—noise, notes, etc.—but nothing that couldn't be handled or dealt with. Bullying wasn't a big issue, except for three or four students with whom he still has run-ins, even today. A lot of our success with school comes down to being on the same page as the teachers. I feel communication, both positive and negative, needs to be kept up all throughout the school year. You have to make yourself known and also be accessible.

Every year, the week before school starts, I call and make arrangements to bring Kyle in for a meeting. We meet his homeroom teacher, pick out his locker and desk, have a look around the classroom, and do a school walk-through to get reacquainted. In the case of a school transition, I make several appointments prior to school closing the year before transfer. Kyle gets to meet anyone with whom he will have contact, gets used to the school setting, and asks any questions or voices any concerns he may have. This routine has worked for us throughout the past years, and we're hoping that it will continue to help make the school setting more comfortable for Kyle. We have always had an after-school routine: come home, get a snack, chat about school and how it went, then sit at the dining room table and complete homework.

Now that I have touched on school, I will touch on Kyle's strengths. Wow! He has so many intellectual strengths and interests: reading, science, facts, anything that will give him information or increase his knowledge. It is unbelievable how much information his mind can absorb. If he doesn't understand something, he has this determination that will keep him at it for hours, until he has it. If Kyle doesn't understand something, he's running to his room to research it until he does. He currently has two new interests: comedy and music. These two have me in tears—of joy!—because they are social activities. He uses comedy to break the ice, and he's at a point now where he is starting to understand jokes and sarcasm and put them in a context where they belong. That is huge! I thought he would never enjoy music because of his sensitive hearing, but country, folk, Irish, and Newfoundland music seem to soothe him.

Kyle wants to be a mechanical engineer, which of course means university. My biggest fear is the thought that he may not get his dream because he won't be able to handle dorms or living in a shared apartment. Will he progress enough by then to interact, handle the noise and social issues, and get himself to class on time? Is this something that our politicians and educators can look into? We definitely need more resources for all autistic students, all the way up through school, but higher education is something that hasn't really been touched on. They have to understand that these students need patience and caring and cannot help blurting out answers or stop when the information starts to flow. They sometimes come off as rude, but they are just being factual.

The best piece of advice I could give to any parent with an autistic child is to tell them to be proud of who the child is, and don't be afraid to tell people the child is autistic, because autism makes them who they are. Don't treat them any differently than the other kids. Sure, you have to make some adjustments, but what applies to one child in our family also applies to Kyle. The consequences are the same. Don't be afraid to say no. Give them chores and responsibility. The accomplishment alone will do wonders for them. And, of course, give them lots of love and hugs.

Here are a few quotes from Kyle himself:

"It's not autism, it's *awesometism*!"

"Being autistic makes me super intelligent. Who wouldn't love that?"

"If you don't want the truth, don't ask me the question!"

"Go ahead, make fun of me. In twenty years, I'll be the whale and you'll be the plankton."

"I think autism is amazing; it makes me who I am."

"If I was like everyone else, the world would be boring."

"Maybe it's us who are normal, and the normal people are different."

"You have to be strong to have autism."

"Being autistic increases my intelligence and makes me the smartest in class."

Kyle's grade four teacher said to him during Autism Awareness Month, "Kyle, I hope they find a cure for autism." Kyle replied, "Why would you say that? I don't!" The teacher asked, "Why not?" And Kyle said, "Then I wouldn't be me, now, would I?"

Two diagnoses—cancer and autism—have taught Dawn Haire-Butt and her family not to sweat the small stuff and to appreciate what they have been given. For Dawn, nothing has been as satisfying as staying at home, advocating for her kids, and enjoying all her family's special moments. Dawn lives with her husband, Peter, and her two children, Kyle and Emily, in Harbour Grace, Newfoundland and Labrador.

My Life with Autism

by B. T. Hall

Brad Hall was born and grew up in Yellowknife, Northwest Territories, where he still lives today. He works for the Department of Education, Culture and Employment (ECE) of the Territorial Government, and he volunteers for Public Works and Services.

Ever since I was young, there has always been something special about me. For instance, I was able to read before I was two years old, having read the letters on an exit sign reflected backwards toward me. I played with toys in an unusual way, sometimes throwing them out of the toy box and climbing into it. I had sensitivities to certain things, like food colourings and preservatives. Some things made me anxious, like Christmas and the events leading to it. Worst of all, people didn't always understand my behaviour when they saw it. It took a while, but on my fourth birthday I was diagnosed with high-functioning autism.

Had I been living in the South, I would have been put in a special needs classroom. Fortunately, the Northwest Territories had fully inclusive schooling, so I went to regular school growing up, sharing a classroom with other children my age. But I worked with an aide, an adult who assists special-needs students in classes. I didn't always understand the work being assigned, so the aide explained it to me, and while many of my classmates became friends of mine, I sometimes had trouble fitting in with them. Arguments sometimes occurred between me and my peers.

When going to and from school, I carried with me something known as a "home-school book," which was essentially a journal or diary for my parents and my school aide. Whatever I did at school on a certain day, good or bad, my aide recorded it in the home-school book, to share with my parents. And whatever I did at home that evening, my parents recorded it in the home-school book, to share with my aide. Having every day of my life watched over like that may seem unnerving now, but it was actually very helpful at the time.

To me, being within the school setting was like being in a distorted reality, separate from the "real world" of my home city. This was even more so during my high school years than during my elementary and middle school years. I did have a soft spot for my home city of Yellowknife growing up, with its unique summer and winter personalities, but whenever I set foot within the doors of my schools, it was like turning off the outside world and entering a semi-isolated yet functional community of its own. It was as though my teachers and fellow students were our own culture, living and working in a unique setting that only we really knew and understood. There were a few things I learned from my peers, such as how to act around others while at school or in public, or what some of their interests were.

Any arguments with my peers and classmates were a relatively rare occurrence. Most of the time, I got along rather well with them. Within my mind, I would often assign some of us into a "five-man (or kid) band," usually but not always with myself as the leader. I would create or envision imaginary adventures and projects for us to take part in. These included owning our own high-rise buildings, making a movie together, or journeying across a fantasy setting by "multi-purpose coach."

My relationships with my peers were just as strong in the real world as they were in my imagination. We would often partake in activities together, or attend events together, or simply talk with each other after class. When I was younger, for instance, I often went to my friends' birthday parties or invited them to mine. As I got older, I played trombone in the school band alongside some other students. During my final year of high school, activities included the Grad Auction, the Christmas Late-Night Event, the Scavenger Hunt, and Dry Grad. I made sure to sign up for whichever of these graduation activities were on whenever possible, so as to work with as many classmates as possible.

I saw graduating from high school not only as an accomplishment, but also as a relief. One stage of my life had finally ended after such a long wait, and another one was beginning. This is not to say that I didn't enjoy certain activities from my time in school, for I did. But after high school graduation, I sought to discover who I truly was and what I truly wanted to do or be.

Not knowing exactly what do with my life at the time, I enrolled at Aurora College Yellowknife Campus in the two years following high school graduation. In the first year, I finished a certificate in management studies. In the second year, I finished a certificate in computing and information systems, which I found more difficult. Management studies had a business side to it, while computing and information systems was more technical. In other words, I found myself better at operating a computer and running its programs than at repairing or assembling a computer.

In many ways, college was not like high school. I got to keep all the textbooks I used, which spared me the additional hassle of trying to return them, or finding them if they got lost. I worked with people of different ages from across the Northwest Territories, rather than with people my own age who were all from Yellowknife. And Computers for Schools, which was a program offered as part of computing and information systems, allowed for a full morning of learning outside the college building.

Rotary Day Canada

After my two years at Aurora College, I enrolled in libraries and information technology at Nova Scotia Community College (NSCC). It was a diploma program, taken entirely online as a distance course so I wouldn't have to physically travel across the country. During my time with NSCC, one of my favourite things to do was talk with my classmates online on the discussion boards. For me, it was much easier than talking with them face to face. With my NSCC course, I could do everything not only from the comfort of my home, but on my own schedule. Well, mostly. There were deadlines to be met with certain assignments and essays, but I didn't have to worry about where I was at the time of day.

While there were some things I disliked, I enjoyed parts of my college years. Most of the good jobs afforded to people of my generation required college diplomas, and being a librarian was less fickle than, say, writing or acting. But I still felt an artistic desire. So to get through my college years and make the most of them, I devoted my time to writing and illustrating my own novella, *Too Many Espresso Beans*. The book was completed about six months before I finished my last class at NSCC, and, not surprisingly, it had autism as a significant theme.

Book launch

Like any emerging, struggling, or aspiring artist, I have been keeping a day job since my late teens. During high school I worked part-time at my local Shoppers Drug Mart. After graduating from high school, I worked as a page at the Yellowknife Public Library, which held my interest. Now my primary workplace is Education, Culture and Employment (ECE), a branch of the Northwest Territories government. Most of my ECE work involves compiling student records from the past into an electronic database.

I also produce and distribute a local twelve-page publication known as the *Coffee Break News*, which has allowed me to develop some skills as an entrepreneur. In addition to retrieving and identifying the content, I design some ads and put the publication together with Adobe InDesign. Through the *Coffee Break News* I have been able to improve my computer skills somewhat, and I have also improved my creative organizational skills. But the best part is getting to deliver the hard copies around town on Fridays. Besides interacting with people and practising my driving, I get to visit various places around town and, as a bonus, I get to have lunch at a different place every week.

Computers have always played a large role in my life. The first computer program I ever used was MacWrite, on a Macintosh 128K. Some of my favourite programs were *Counting Critters, Picture Chompers, Odell Lake, The Oregon Trail, Cross Country Canada, Little Red Wagon, GeoGenius World, Thinkin' Things Collection 2, Virtual Pool, Dragon's Challenge*, and *Mavis Beacon Teaches Typing*. Sometime after getting to know computers, I got to know the Internet. Besides setting up an email account, I soon got hooked on using certain websites for research. In fact, I have made it one of my life plans to go through every person on the Internet Movie Database, and I have gotten as far as Isa Barzizza.

My favourite aspect of the Internet thus far has been social networking. Immediately upon graduation from high school, I registered for Classmates.com so I could communicate with my former classmates, but I never really used that site, and it was shortly thereafter that Facebook came along. On Facebook, I "friended" as many people as I could. I started with family members and then moved on to old friends and former classmates. The first game I played on Facebook was FarmVille, but when I started playing multiple games on Facebook they became time-consuming, so I withdrew. I later used LinkedIn, once again connecting with close friends and relations. After eventually withdrawing from LinkedIn, I signed up for Twitter. Twitter may have been my favourite social networking site, since I could safely follow or be followed by complete strangers. It made me feel like a celebrity, allowing me to promote my works publicly. But eventually I decided I'd had enough of Twitter, and so I withdrew from it.

Like the rest of us, my life has been full of what I call honours and disappointments. My greatest honour was in 2013, when I got to be the best man at my brother's wedding in Strathmore. My second-greatest honour came in 2003, when I won the Northwest Territories Outstanding Youth Volunteer of the Year Award. My third-greatest honour came later that same year, when I graduated from high school along with all my peers. My greatest disappointment was in 2004, when I tried out for a North America–wide Archie Comics talent search that never really went anywhere. My second-greatest disappointment was in 2011, when I submitted *Too Many Espresso Beans* to four different publishers and they each turned it down.

Having struggled with autism my entire life, I could definitely say that it has its advantages and disadvantages. One advantage of my autism is that I have an amazing memory for rote facts. That is, I am able to remember certain things with extreme accuracy. During my time in school, for instance, I was able to memorize all the teachers' names, and when I graduated from high school, I was able to list the entire roster of students who graduated with me. In fact, remembering lists seems to be a specialty of mine. One of the earliest lists I memorized was the entire cast of the movie *Mary Poppins*. Other lists I memorized later in life included the flags of certain countries, and the order of cars on certain trains.

Meals on Wheels

One disadvantage of my autism is how easily agitated certain things sometimes make me. For instance, when I realize I have forgotten to bring something with me, I often go into a panic. Then, if possible, I simply try to dash back to where I came from and pick it up. What's worse, for a long time I had trouble telling people where I was going. I lacked certain social skills and could not understand the feelings of other people. Oftentimes when I went somewhere, I did not say where, so the people I was with did not know where I had gone, and they often worried for my safety.

I love to travel, and I have been doing so for much of my life. I always find it exciting whenever I travel, and each portion of the journey is a unique experience in itself. But for me the important part of travelling is being equipped and prepared. If I do not fully understand the setting or the events, or do not have a certain item with me, I may become agitated. But if I have everything I need, and know exactly what is going on, I will be likely to enjoy myself. Visiting new places is one thing that makes my travel exciting. There are places I have not yet visited but would like to, such as Australia.

For a long time I had trouble with change. I thrived on routine and liked it when things stayed the same. Starting elementary school and finishing high school made me feel somewhat uneasy, as did coping with the changes brought on by my parents' divorce. Whenever something significant was going to change in my life, a discussion regarding the change helped me cope with anxiety. It also helped to meet any new people I would be working with, or visit the place I would be working in. My ability to deal with change got better over time with these tools, and certain events no longer make me throw an obsessive fit.

For most people, adulthood means leaving home, moving out on your own, and becoming completely independent of your parents, but since I have autism, I still require support, which is provided mainly by my mother. Should anything happen to my mother, I am counting on my brother to be my primary support person. I do not plan on having children of my own; I simply could not handle it. Also, one of my life plans is to remain single forever.

I hope not only to build on the things I have done, but also to continue new things. I hope the good parts of my autism help me pursue my interests. Like race, religion, or gender, I feel that autism is something to be embraced.

B. T. Hall represents the Northwest Territories on the Autism Canada Advisory Committee of Adults with Autism Spectrum Disorder. He assembles and distributes a local publication known as the Coffee Break News, *and in 2009 he self-published his novella,* Too Many Espresso Beans.

Putting a Recreation Perspective into the Spectrum

by Heather Warner

Heather Warner is a nationally certified therapeutic recreation specialist (CTRS) who has worked as a camp counsellor at several camps for children and adults with autism. She has worked as a behaviour therapist and is now employed as an early childhood therapist.

My interest in working with individuals living with developmental disabilities began during my high school years and carried over to college at the University of North Carolina at Wilmington. There, I elected recreational therapy as my major. Now, after graduating with a bachelor's degree, I am a nationally certified therapeutic recreation specialist currently working as an early childhood therapist and school-aged instructor for children on the autism spectrum.

I currently work in two different centre-based programs for children with an autism diagnosis. All therapists and instructors work on a ratio of 1:1 with students and help each student reach goals as assigned by the board certified behaviour analyst (BcBA) and head teacher of each program. All school-aged students at the centre have come to the centre because of behaviour issues in the classrooms at a typical school. The centre provides behavioural supports for both parents and students alike. Through my experience and prior education, I am pursuing occupational therapy, working with children on the autism spectrum as a career for the future. As I continue to learn more about the ever-changing diagnosis of autism, I bring with me not only my formal training and participation in sports, both coaching children and participating in varsity teams, but also experiences at summer camps, and now the school setting.

Andrew Shinbara before one of his many baseball games. Photo courtesy of Christy Shinbara, Andrew's mother.

Formal and Informal Learning

My major in recreational therapy combined aspects of recreation with physical therapy, occupational therapy, and psychology, focusing on the needs of those with disabilities. I learned to pay close attention to the whole person, from physical needs and wishes to changing emotions during recreational and other activities, and to adapt these activities for individual needs and desires. As such, recreational therapists can play significant roles in a wide variety of settings with a diverse population of clients.

An especially important part of my education, which has led me to want to work with individuals on the autism spectrum for the rest of my life, was training and employment as a counsellor at two different summer camps. The first was a day camp for those aged between six and twenty-one years with developmental and physical disabilities. The second was an overnight camp catering to any individual with a primary diagnosis on the autism spectrum.

Learning at Camp Royall

"Camp Royall," in North Carolina, is specifically geared toward those with some degree of autism (http://autismsociety-nc.org/index.php/get-help/camproyallinfo). It is an exceptional place because no level of autism is denied and each camper is recognized for his or her uniqueness. Working there in the summer of 2013 definitely changed my life, as I now call this the happiest and most accepting place for campers with disabilities. As a recreation therapy major and a previous camp counsellor, I had been introduced to the characteristic features of autism, so I thought I knew about autism, but at Camp Royall I was astonished by the amount of information that I lacked, the huge amount of ongoing research, and the information that was still needed to understand such a complex disorder.

Starting our initial week of training, we were expected to view each day from the mind of a child or adult with autism. A variety of resources offered insights into what it must be like for those with autism: for instance, parents spoke about their children, and several documentaries explained life on the autism spectrum. We learned information about triggers for negative behaviours, positive reinforcement, and many other strategies for working with children and adults on the spectrum. I remember constantly thinking about how the autistic mind worked, even after our days of training were over, and tried to wrap my brain around the grey areas that are still undiscovered. I realized that individuals on the autism spectrum react to situations in different ways than typically developing people because their brains use different ways to process internal and external information. For example, some individuals are comforted by repeating certain phrases that they hear in movies or TV shows, whereas others are fascinated by the workings of toys, the way the grass grows in the ground, or the way the fan spins on the ceiling. It was, and still is, challenging to understand exactly what each person's reactions mean, but it was so rewarding and fascinating to figure it out for each activity each day. Their responses and reactions, whether verbal or non-verbal, gave clues to their wants, needs, and emotions toward a specific activity.

One of the cabins that campers stay in during their week at Camp Royall. Photo courtesy of Autism Society of North Carolina.

I learned that in a world that is already overwhelming for the general population, individuals on the spectrum often have a hard time focusing on simple tasks or directions; noises, people, or other environmental triggers become distractions and cause the brain to go into overdrive, also known as overstimulation. For instance, the sound of an air conditioner or a fan may be so overwhelming that it distracts the individual from anything communicated from a caregiver or therapist. In such a case, noise-cancelling headphones can be helpful to muffle external sounds and avoid overstimulation. Other strategies to avoid overstimulation include head squeezes (a caregiver will gently squeeze the head of the individual in order to apply necessary pressure), joint compressions (applying pressure to joints to relieve tense muscles), squeeze toys (which allow these individual to relieve energy in a safe way), and vestibular motor activities like swinging or jumping on a trampoline.

From day one at Camp Royall, I realized the importance of a positive attitude, contagious smile, patience, and a schedule of activities for the day. A positive attitude from the counsellor allowed campers to feel more at ease so they were then able to build rapport. A child or adult who was higher-functioning on the autism spectrum may have written their own schedule and checked off each activity after it was over, whereas someone on the lower end of the spectrum, maybe non-verbal, would use a "first-then" schedule, or a schedule with pictures that showed only a few activities at one time.

Andrew Shinbara running the bases during one of his games. It displays his enthusiasm for his sport and social skills with others by giving high fives on his way to home plate. Photo courtesy of Christy Shinbara, Andrew's mother.

To clarify, a "first-then" schedule is a board (invariably a laminated piece of cardstock paper) with the words "first" and "then" side by side (or one above the other). Velcro circles are placed on the picture of the activity at hand and attached to the board to display the schedule. The counsellor puts the schedule on the board using appropriate pictures and makes sure the camper understands what the activities will be. For example, if campers were going to the pool and then changing out of their swimsuits, the schedule would read "first pool," "then clothes." Breaking down the schedule into two different activities, even if they are very simple, allows the camper to focus on two things only, rather than being overwhelmed or anxious over a whole day's list of activities or a whole day of unknowns. When showing them the schedule, I would repeat the order of the activities between two and four times by pointing and saying what they were, until I felt the camper understood by moving toward the first activity. I would give more processing time, if needed, before using physical or gestural prompts to help campers get to the activity at hand. I noticed that children and adults became less anxious about activities when they knew what they were doing in the future.

Other campers used a picture schedule with four to five activities at a time. The activities were either simple stick figures (a symbol of the activity) or actual pictures of the activity. The pictures had the name of the activity written underneath.

The inside of the cabin at Camp Royall. Campers each have their own bunk bed and share a bathroom with other campers. Photo courtesy of Autism Society of North Carolina.

Many campers responded well to this format, as they could look at a picture, showing what was happening next, rather than reading words. Campers who displayed negative behaviours, or refused to participate in activities after being told, responded well to pictures of activity to reinforce our expectations. If a camper did not like arts and crafts and threw a tantrum, I would add an activity—places or items he or she enjoys—to work toward. A common example of preferred items or activities might be taking a movement break, like walking, playing with a sensory-related toy, colouring, etc. These preferred activities reinforced the idea that we were going to try the non-preferred activity first and then move onto a more pleasurable one. In the event that a wanted or preferred item is too far in the future, other sensory needs could be met throughout the non-preferred activity. For a camper who is overstimulated in an activity, head squeezes, joint compressions, or squeeze toys can be given periodically to prevent escalated behaviours. Revisiting the end reward after giving sensory stimulation is also helpful to keep an individual on task. Anxiety levels went down with scheduling, and activities were accomplished that parents, family, or therapists had never seen before. It was rewarding to be able to tell parents about these new activities, and the camper displayed greater self-confidence.

A Structured Approach

Camp Royall is noted for its extremely structured approach. I did not realize how much structure is needed for those on the autism spectrum. Each activity was scheduled for no longer than thirty minutes (except for the pool, everyone's favourite, which was scheduled for forty-five minutes). This was ideal for most campers as attention spans tended to get shorter toward the end of the hour. Scheduling not only reduced anxieties about non-preferred activities, but also assisted with difficult transitions from a preferred activity. It allowed campers to know exactly what their day was going to look like.

This is an example of one of the group activities at Camp Royall. We start every day with songs that campers can sing and dance to. It helps us start each day with a positive attitude and enthusiasm to get us through the day! Photo courtesy of Autism Society of North Carolina.

Every activity was also structured. For example, gym time was split up into three different activities: walking or running around the perimeter of the gym, stretches and games, followed by choice time. Each activity was long enough to complete, but short enough to remain engaged in without frustration. I learned that structure was essential for many individuals since it allowed counsellors to introduce new activities, some of which became preferred.

Positive Reinforcement

Going hand in hand with structure and schedules, counsellors at Camp Royall were taught how to use positive reinforcement and a "strength-based" approach. The latter involved finding an individual's strengths, either from parents or from observation during activities. The beginning of a camp week was often a special challenge, as transitioning to camp life was sometimes difficult for campers. However, as the second and third days went by, strengths became obvious. With these strengths identified, it was easier to incorporate positive reinforcement with challenging activities. If a camper did not want to participate in an activity, or if they displayed negative behaviours toward themselves or someone else, it was better to show or tell them an appropriate way to behave. This is the preferable way to use positive reinforcement and redirection, as continuing to say "no" or "don't" makes situations even more challenging.

The gym at Camp Royall. It is a great space for all special events and can be easily structured to cater to each camper's needs. Photo courtesy of Autism Society of North Carolina.

If hitting is used to communicate an idea, it is important to recognize the campers' needs or wants. However, finding these is challenging and it may not happen. Then, it may be best to give campers something else to do with their hands to replace such behaviour, until they are calm, then try to figure out needs or wants. Giving them a squeeze toy may be one way to control hitting, or talking about and looking at "nice hands." "Nice hands" involves holding your hands together in front of your body and squeezing them together. This allows the camper to get sensory stimulation from themselves, rather than hitting something or someone for sensory needs.

Show and tell campers what they *can* do instead of what they can't. Repeatedly saying "no" can lead to more negative behaviours that may be mere attempts to communicate. I have also noticed that if negative behaviours continue even after counsellors have shown the appropriate ways of communicating, maybe there is something else that the camper would like to say or do. If this is the case, it is okay to let the individuals show you what they want. You can do this by verbally prompting, saying "show me what you want" and allowing them to guide you to the activity. If it is something that is not what the camper is supposed to be doing, give them another option and explain why that is not a choice right now. If appropriate, the wanted or preferred activity can be revisited at a different time.

A vestibular motor activity at Camp Royall. It is called the zap line and is not only fun for campers, but also gives them sensory stimulation. Photo courtesy of Autism Society of North Carolina.

For example, if we are in arts and crafts and the camper would like to be in the sensory room instead, we could show them that first they do arts and crafts for five minutes, and then they can go to the sensory room. Negative behaviours in response to this approach can and do happen frequently, as the camper obviously wants something different than the task at hand. To deal with this, show and tell them how much time they have left and honour their choice once the time is up. Time can be shown in several ways: using a timer, telling them what needs to be done in the first activity, or giving tokens as the task at hand is being completed. It is important that individuals on the spectrum try new activities, even if it may be difficult for both the campers and staff members, because it exposes them to new learning experiences. This exposure will hopefully reduce anxieties toward novel places and help individuals problem-solve for the future. Of course, if the novel situation causes extreme anxiety, discomfort, or leads to negative behaviours, it is best to remove individuals from the situation and let them calm down in a place they enjoy. Even exposure to a new environment for one minute in the beginning may lead to a day where the individual is okay with staying there for longer.

Some campers and staff members fishing at the pond at Camp Royall. Several adaptations are made depending on the need of the camper. Photo courtesy of Autism Society of North Carolina.

Positive reinforcement can also come in other ways, such as a reward or token system, commonly used at Camp Royall where the outcome is an activity or thing that the camper looks forward to. A reward system works in a way that resembles the "first-then" schedules. Campers work toward a goal. For instance, perhaps a camper really enjoys playing on the iPod or responds well to fruit snacks after activities. In these instances, there will be a number of "tokens" with Velcro that can be earned during activities and added onto the board. Below is an example of one type of token system.

A camper needs to earn five stars in order to get the iPod at the end. A star can be earned by acting in an appropriate manner, which includes: listening or engaging in an activity for five minutes, sitting nicely in their chair, or using a quiet voice when appropriate. Once campers continue to do the preferred behaviour during the activity, they can be rewarded with further stars until they have enough for the grand reward.

Of course, this is only an example of what a token system can be used for. I had success with this system for campers who displayed negative behaviours toward certain activities, such as yelling and hitting instead of working on an art activity, or a camper who refused to do the activity. I continued to give stars to them for positive behaviours. If the activity involved gluing, cutting, and colouring, I could give a star for each step until the activity had been completed. The reward will then be given and the token system will be reset for the next activity. It is a great idea to use this system for non-preferred activities, wait time (unstructured time), transitioning, and for building rapport with individuals who may be hard to reach.

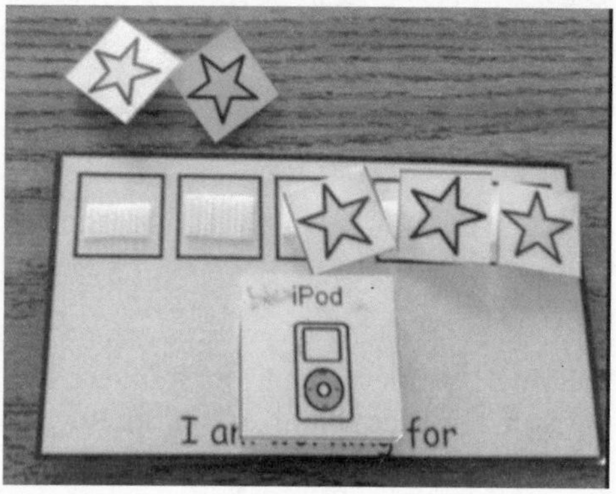

Time is Needed

While my time at Camp Royall was incredibly rewarding, the time we had with each camper was frustratingly short, and I was never sure whether the positive changes we saw lasted past each camp session. I realized this again when, during the summer of 2014, I was hired as a behaviour therapist for a summer camp for children and young adults on the autism spectrum. It was a community-based program where we took our campers into the community to work on different goals. Every behaviour therapist was assigned one camper and was expected to help campers accomplish assigned goals—cognitive, communication, physical, etc.—over the course of the summer. My time at camp was again very rewarding, as I was assigned to work with a bright young man named Andrew. He is a seventeen-year-old boy diagnosed on the higher end of the autism spectrum. I had the chance to really get to know Andrew, since our time together was much longer than that at Camp Royall.

Andrew

In the first week of camp, I built rapport with Andrew by finding his strengths and weaknesses. I quickly realized that he was full of energy, one of his major strengths. On the first day of camp, he quickly said "Hi" and immediately began playing with the toys he could find. His laugh echoed all the way from the back room as I could hear him joking around with another camper.

Andrew's goals focused on learning to interact with others in a community setting. The goals included: initiating and telling me his wants and needs using his words, safety awareness in the community, recognizing and acknowledging other individuals that he knew, and being aware of his personal hygiene needs. I focused on all goals every day just to be sure he was understanding and aware of his surroundings in the community.

Andrew's language and recognition of hygiene needs were two of the major goals I focused on as being essential for his future. His limited vocabulary and limited speech hindered his communication in a community. However, with several prompts and assistance, he was able to let me know his basic wants and needs. (For example, rather than using American sign language or gestural prompting, he learned to use words to ask for help.) Andrew also found it very challenging to tell and express his bathroom and hygiene needs. In this scenario, I played a crucial role in enabling his independence, using positive language to show the bathroom was not scary and giving him rewards for using it in the appropriate manner.

His safety awareness was the third concern, as he would often dart into the parking lot without being aware of cars or others around him. In crowded areas, like the bowling alley, I helped him pay special attention to his speed when he was walking and helped him safely navigate through groups of people. This improved as the summer continued and he was more aware in crowded scenarios.

After talking to his mother and learning more about Andrew, I found he was a unique person with incredible talent and love for life despite a multiplicity of medical issues. Andrew is not only on the autism spectrum, but he is also diagnosed with Rubenstein-Taybi syndrome, seizure disorder, ADHD, severe asthma, and sensory issues. In fact, it was only when he was about eight years old that he was diagnosed with autism. During his preschool and early elementary school days, he was deaf and used only sign language to communicate and read. As he grew older, his hearing improved, although he is still learning how to use his voice instead of just signs. This is definitely a challenge for him, but it does not stop him from doing what he loves.

After I recognized his love of sports, his mother told me Andrew had been an active participant in Special Olympics basketball, bowling, hand cycling, and soccer. He started playing all of these sports as soon as he was eligible (at age four). His love for being active in group settings and interacting with others has taught him about appropriate ways to be social. I believe his active lifestyle has contributed significantly to helping him become the caring and compassionate teenager that he is. From my recreation therapy degree and my sports background, Andrew and I connected with ease. He was able to teach me about baseball, and I used my experience in coaching soccer to teach him a few new moves and game tactics.

Andrew's empathy and sympathy for others extends well beyond the "typical" or "stereotypical" diagnosis for autism. Most individuals who don't know autism think that there is a lack of empathy or sympathy. I do not believe this. Every time we went on our trips into the community, Andrew was always sharing toys with others, finding new friends to play with, and making sure that everyone was okay. He would often show concern for those who were coughing, sneezing, or said "ouch!" when something hurt, by giving a hug and asking if they were okay. I think that he had a strong ability to understand others' needs and concerns and was always willing to help out.

Andrew's love for life was another huge strength that even changed the way I view the world. Even through his anxieties in crowded situations or paying attention to his surroundings, Andrew loved every activity we did. He would always find a way to laugh and smile about the activity at hand. For example, when we would go to the pool, the lazy river never failed to make his laugh echo across the pool. He really enjoyed walking around the river as fast as possible, making it seem like he was opening Christmas presents on Christmas Day. His positive attitude, and contagious laugh in every community setting, made me realize that life is not as serious as we all take it sometimes.

Lessons Learned

My education and early experiences in learning about children and adults with diverse autistic behaviours has provided me with many important lessons and insights. Above all, there are difficulties in communication, between the counsellor, the caregiver, the teacher, and the individual with autism. Hence, it is important to allow the individual with autism time to process requests and directives. For example, if one is asking someone with autism what they want to do next, allow extra time—a "wait-time" technique—for a response, even while appreciating that waiting for an answer in silence can be challenging in our contemporary society that is focused so much on immediacy.

It is also important to allow choices each day, because it allows individuals to feel independent and in control of their day, reducing anxieties. As a caregiver or therapist, it is imperative that you are able to honour the choice that the individual decides upon. In other words, if you are allowing a choice between listening to music and playing on the iPad, it is important to have both ready and to be satisfied with either choice. The inability of a therapist or caregiver to follow through with the individual's choice may lead to negative behaviours and thus cause more distress. Along with offering choices, it is important to recognize that the individual may not want either choice you are offering, so it is best to provide a "none of these" or "different" option.

Another prevalent communication problem is when too many words are used in questions or too many questions are asked without processing time. Negative behaviours, such as hitting, pinching, biting, punching, or refusal can occur in these circumstances. Breaking down language into the simplest sentences allows the individual to process your demand or request (ex: first . . . then). In this case, there should be no extra words that the individual needs to sift through in order to figure out the message being relayed. As I have continued to use this wait-time technique, I have noticed a decrease in the number of meltdowns and tantrums over simple requests or questions.

In conjunction with the above suggestion for processing time, I have also noticed that many children communicate in behavioural responses. This adds another challenge to an already complex disorder, as behaviours can be interpreted as avoidance or a form of communication, depending on the circumstance. For instance, one child continued to hit and attempt to bite me while he was colouring. I was confused because he was calm while colouring, but as soon as he was done with one colour, he hit or attempted to bite me. I picked up on this communication and tried to figure out what was bothering him. As a trial-and-error technique, I removed certain items from the situation and added some structural components. I tried removing all distractions on the table (extra crayons and markers, other colouring pages, bins of glue, etc.) and tried to redirect him back to the colouring page. When this didn't work, I tried a new tactic. I showed him what to colour on the page with his crayon. I then picked out the colour he needed to use and where on the page he should be using it. This trial-and-error scenario was successful and he really enjoyed colouring after that, without negative behaviour.

Difficulty with communication also affects individuals who are non-verbal or lower-functioning on the autism spectrum. It is hard for caregivers to imagine exactly what these children are thinking at the time they are asked a question. Most of the time, these individuals know more than we are aware. Delayed processing and constant distractions from the environment muffle their ability to comprehend complex phrases and questions. I imagine it is like standing at a concert in a crowd of people with the music playing loudly and having someone ask me to solve a complicated mathematical problem within a minute. Impossible! But, if I was placed in a silent room and given a piece of paper with the mathematical problem written on it, it would be much easier to complete this task. I constantly think about analogies like this and try to imagine myself in the mind of someone with autism. I see each autistic brain as wired differently, as each individual reacts to situations in a different fashion. Therefore, using simple language, giving processing time, being aware of the environment, and waiting are key to receiving answers to questions and avoiding negative behaviours. A smile or laugh may even occur when these individuals understand that you are reading their behaviours and making necessary adjustments.

It is important to understand an individual's thought processes in the surrounding environment, especially when approaching new situations. It could be cluttered, maybe too noisy, maybe a change from normal, etc. Many times, individuals with autism prefer that their environment stay the same, as change can be frightening. I have learned by trial and error to adapt the environment, to make it more suitable. Transitions to the new environment may be easier with support, such as sensory stimulation (joint compressions, headphones, squeeze toys, breaks from new environment, etc.) or a schedule or structure. Having a familiar item or person in the new environment will also ease the transition, reducing negative behaviours. So, rather than shying away from negative behaviour or constantly thinking it is a problem, I try to redirect it to something positive by remembering to show or tell the correct way to complete activities. Also, as a caregiver, it is beneficial to pick up on common behaviours associated with certain situations, so that the environment can be set up ahead of time.

While trial and error is invaluable, it has its frustrations. What I mean is, one day you may redirect behaviour to a preferred activity several times and it may work with ease. The next day, it may not and you will have to find a new way. What works one day may not work another, so I have an open mind to trying new things as I always remind myself that all children and adult have their "off days." You may also have a child with very similar behaviours and characteristics as another and you may try the same tactic to redirect negative behaviours; it may work, but it may not. When frustrations dampen my day, I try to remember that my failure is in not uncovering the characteristics of the person I am trying to help.

I also remember my training in recreation therapy to find appropriate recreation activities. Sometimes, all the individual needs is a movement break from the task at hand. For example, taking a walk, bouncing on a yoga ball, or dancing to music are great recreation activities that also help with sensory input needs. The break is long enough to allow the mind relief, but short enough that the transition back to the task at hand is not difficult.

Laughs and smiles were abundant at Camp Royall, as counsellors were always in high spirits and viewed each other and campers in the most positive light. At the beginning of training, we also learned how to have lots of patience, especially when it came to wait time. Our successes in letting campers have the necessary time they needed resulted in an abundance of smiles, laughs, joy, and, most of all, accomplishments in completing all daily activities. The positive energy that surrounded each camper was contagious and helped campers feel comfortable, minimizing anxieties. Camp Royall is a very special place for this reason, and it has taught me that individuals on the spectrum are just like any typical developing children in that they can read into your mood that day. If you are showing that you are frustrated, they will pick up on it and may even cause you more frustration. Thus, creating a positive environment full of enjoyable recreational activities decreases negative behaviours.

The sign that sits at the front of the camp. It is a great introduction to the start of a week at camp. Photo courtesy of Autism Society of North Carolina.

Working with autistic children, adolescents, and adults is like playing a game of Monopoly. Each time you play, you earn a different amount of money, you own different properties, you play with different people; everything about each game is different. However, each step of the way around the board gets you that much closer to passing "Go." You may lose some money one time and have to figure out a way to make it work the next time around. Maybe you have to sell one of your properties; maybe you start trying to wish for a certain number on the dice. Whatever you decide to do, you know that you will make it around the board for the next time. Every day I work with these children is different and always gives me a new perspective on the way they perceive the world around them. Each day, I know I want to bring them the joy they deserve so that they can make it around the board and collect their $200 at the end of the day. I enjoy the challenge of figuring out what makes them tick and figuring out if I need to take away something from their environment, similar to selling properties, or, if I need to give them space, similar to taking a coffee break in Monopoly.

Heather Warner's current job entails working one on one with children between the ages of two and six in intense therapy sessions. The therapy sessions focus on using applied behavioural analysis (ABA) to help ready children for school and their future. She is directly supervised by a board certified behaviour analyst (BcBA), who creates goals for each child and develops behaviour plans to reduce negative behaviours. She is planning on attending graduate school in the near future, either for occupational therapy or for certification in ABA therapy.

No Such Word as "Can't"

by Laura Hamlyn

Laura Hamlyn is the mother of three children with three different sets of disabilities—autism, ADHD/asthma, and dwarfism. She works full-time and does her best to make sure her family is well cared for. Her family may be a little different than some, she says, but they are a positive force that will make anyone smile. They never give up and never say, "I can't."

Autism is a word that most people view with sympathy. The reality is autism has affected our little family, and to be completely honest, it is a blessing in a way. On January 2, 2004, my beautiful baby daughter was born. Kara Janet Lee was two weeks overdue. It was suspected she had been living without water surrounding her for at least a week. The first day she came into this world, she started off with a low heart rate and purple, leathery hands and feet. Born in Labrador City, Kara had her first plane ride on an air ambulance at a mere eleven hours old to St. John's, Newfoundland, due to the lack of medical capabilities in our community. Kara was housed in the neonatal intensive care unit (NICU) at the Janeway Children's Hospital for the first few days of her life for precautionary purposes.

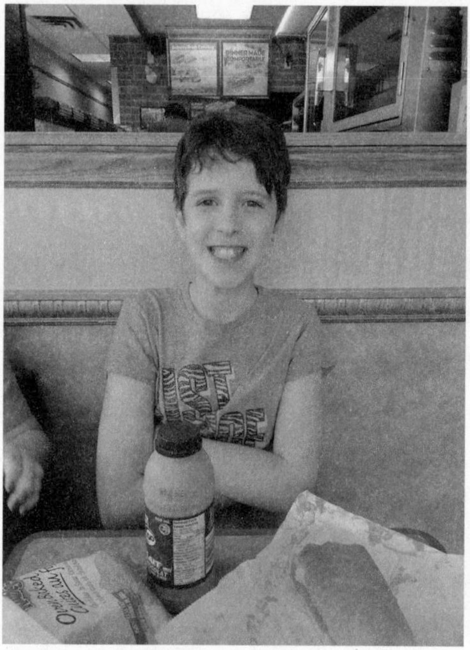

Kara Janet Lee at ten years old, beautiful inside and out. August 2014.

At five days old, Kara came back home to Labrador City, and it was amazing to watch her grow. Within the first couple of months in her little life, I noticed a few things different than what I had experienced with my other two children. At four months old, Kara was already saying Mom, Dad, Nan, and Pop. She was a very happy-go-lucky baby.

By the time Kara was fifteen months old, she had finally started to walk. However, her vocabulary did not expand further than the few words she had first spoken when she was only a few months old. By the time she was two years old, she still spoke very little, and it was noticeable, in her reactions to different situations, that something was not quite "normal." Kara had a tendency to tippytoe when she walked. When she was excited for any reason, good or bad, she would flap her hands. When she was frustrated trying to explain something to us with the few words she knew, and we could not understand what she meant, Kara would bang her little fists against the sides of her face and would leave bruises on her cheeks. She would sometimes go beyond self-abuse to hitting her brother and sister. The social skills that children develop were not there. Kara was prone to playing by herself. Kara loved hugs, but she would not let you kiss her, much less kiss you back.

Because Kara was not learning quite as fast as her brother and sister had, I took her to a public health worker, only to be told that children learn at different paces in life, and if this persisted by the time Kara was three years old the issue would be looked into further.

Just a couple weeks before Kara turned three, I took her grocery shopping along with her babysitter and my other two children. The realization of how difficult things were for Kara in a social environment became very apparent. As it was Christmas season, the mall was a very busy spot, and, of course, loud. When visiting the mall and being placed in a cart, Kara had a habit of taking off her boots. It was some sort of comfort to her, and I didn't mind as long as she was happy. However, this time, while we were at the checkout at the grocery store, Kara kept asking for something out of the $300 worth of groceries that were being placed in bags. That started an emotional state I will never forget. Tears streamed down her cheeks, and with each tear her frustration mounted, until she went into a full-fledged tantrum in the middle of the store. She beat her little face so hard it was heart-wrenching. I wrapped my arms around my little girl while a friend tried to put Kara's boots back on her feet. She was in such a state there was no success getting the boots back on her, or in calming her in any way.

After paying for the groceries, I took Kara and my children out of the store into the mall, which was a confusion of people. I tried dealing with Kara while still wrapping my arms around her, but she continued to punch herself in frustration, trying to desensitize herself from whatever mental state she had herself in. I could hear whispers on either side of me: "If that were my child, I would . . ." "What kind of mother is she?" "Someone should take those children away from her." Finally, having spent years in torment, desperate for answers, trying my hardest to make things work, I broke. Right where I was, I started to cry. I kept on walking, pushing the cart, and I didn't care who saw how upset I was.

I had held things in long enough trying to figure out a way to help my daughter. As a single mother of three children, I needed help and I was determined to get it. Kara needed to grow, expand beyond her capabilities. I knew she could, but I knew there was more happening here. My cousin came over one day and sat me down. She had brought over a list of questions and asked me to answer them as honestly as I could. Each question was about symptoms Kara showed, with similarities to those for being autistic. Most of the questions my cousin asked pertained to the way Kara was acting. That was when I made the doctor's appointment for her.

Not long after Kara turned three, I took her to our family doctor in Labrador City. The issues were not getting any easier. The self-abuse and the physical abuse against her brother and sister were becoming more frequent, and the vocabulary she had once learned had reverted to nothing more than saying, "Spiderman can too," which meant everything from "I am hungry" to "Let's play." She spoke no other words.

When the doctor walked into his office on that fateful day, Kara was sitting on his heater. She did not want to sit on a chair. He asked her questions, only to get a sidelong glance from her as she could not look him in the eyes. When he saw her sensory issues starting to develop and she started to bang her head off the wall, he made a referral for her to see a specialist in St. John's for further testing. This was the beginning of the help she needed.

Within a couple of months, Kara and I went to the Janeway once again for her to go see various doctors. The appointments were thorough. Eye tests, hearing tests, an EEG, and a cardiology appointment were all a part of her visit. Kara also saw the specialist for autism. Twice. Once the appointments were over and we met with the specialist the second time, we were told it looked like Kara may have autism. We had to book further appointments to get more testing done within the next couple of months.

It was nice to know we were finally getting somewhere with this. Someone finally believed in us and was willing to help. While we were in between a "maybe" and a "she is autistic" diagnosis, back home in Labrador, a friend suggested I cut off Kara's hair. Kara was always pushing it out of the way, and it seemed to bother her the same way running your nails across a chalkboard does most people. So, being a stubborn lady, I did just that. I sat down in my living room, while Kara sat in front of me, and every curly lock she had was cut off. With her hair cut above her ears, I simply prayed that it would help.

Within a week of the haircut, Kara started saying more words, and she even started on sentences. It was amazing to watch. I sat her on my lap and sang to her the way I always had, and she started to sing back—full songs, pitch perfect.

About a month later, we went back to St. John's again for her final diagnosis. Yes, Kara had autism. I guess the doctors who told me expected a different reaction from me. All I could say was, "At least we know what is happening and can get her the help she needs. Yes, Kara may have autism, but that is not who she is, that is simply the challenge she faces. Her name is Kara."

After we came back from that trip to St. John's, within a week I had a house filled with specialists to help get Kara on the right track to the best life we could provide for her. It was a little overwhelming at first. However, it was the best thing that ever happened for our family, especially for Kara.

From learning what an individual support services planning (ISSP) team is all about, and being a part of it to help assess the strengths and needs, hiring people to work with Kara, and weekly visits from the Department of Child, Youth and Family Services' behavioural department for extra help and assessments for the skills she was learning, and providing new information for new skill sets for her to learn, it became apparent that our lives were changing in a drastic way for the next couple of years.

I will not say it was the easiest thing in the world to have my home filled with different people working with my child. I had my good days and bad days. It was good most of the time. There were days that felt as though I should have been able to do this on my own. I felt like less of a parent because I had so many people working to get Kara to where she is today. I missed having a family life. What I didn't realize at those times was that I was lucky to have more people working with Kara. Our family extended out past just our bloodline. So many more people helped us get Kara on track. We had opportunities many people simply did not have.

Direct home services of the Child, Youth and Family Services offered to send Kara to nursery school. It was a great opportunity for her to learn social skills. Her first day of school I had a phone call that was mortifying at the time, but it's funny now. Kara could not and would not wear anything wet or dirty at all. That day in school she played with some toy involving water, got wet, and stripped buck naked in the classroom full of students. When I got the call, all I could do was grab her clothes, go to school, and get her dressed. They had a costume on her when I arrived, to at least keep her covered. Thankfully the teacher—also the parent of a child with autism—handled the situation like a pro.

At the end of the school year, Kara was ready for her first graduation. She still struggled with being around crowds, so this day was sure to provoke some of her sensory issues. Kara did wonderfully, sitting up on stage with the rest of her class. When Kara's name was called to go get her diploma and people clapped for her success, however, she was overwhelmed. The hand flapping and tippytoeing began, along with falling to the ground in tears and banging her fists against her face. Yes, she was in therapy, but her moments were still there. This just showed us where she needed extra help.

By the time she started kindergarten, Kara was ready. She had a student assistant to work with her in the areas she found difficult, as she needed help staying on topic and completing tasks. The extra help she received was amazing. To see her socialize with her classmates was great. She did, however, say things as she saw them, literally. It would be normal for her to notice, for example, a certain way someone chewed their food, and say to them that they "ate weird." That became an issue pretty quickly. We had to teach Kara to compliment, not critique. Kara said what she saw without a filter. It was a bit trying to get her to understand what she should and should not say, but not impossible. Within a few months, Kara was complimenting everyone some way or another, which she continues to do today.

Our family has the motto, "There is no such word as *can't*." Kara had skating as a school activity one day. She had never done it before and she was scared. She was scheduled to go skating that afternoon, so I kept her home from school in the morning to calm her fears. I had her put her skates on in the house. I put her on the carpeted part of the house, held her hands, and got her to skate. It worked for her. When she went skating that afternoon with the school, she was not afraid anymore. A little extra help and guidance was all she needed.

Denika, Kara, and Matthew enjoying a bit of fun at Margaret Bowater Park in Corner Brook. June 2014.

In 2011, our family moved from Labrador City to Corner Brook, Newfoundland. At the age of seven, Kara had to face a change, something that was very difficult for her at the time. She liked things to be a certain way. It was not an easy task to get her used to something new in her life, but it was a beneficial one. It took Kara quite a while to accept the changes at first, but she has come to accept changes more easily with time.

Kara had, in my opinion, the greatest help she could have received, and she continues to get the help she needs in the school system. We have known from the day she went to kindergarten she was not going to graduate from school with a high school diploma, but she will receive a certificate of completion. We could look at this as a negative thing, but I don't. I believe that after she finishes school she can always go back and get her diploma elsewhere.

She has hopes and dreams of working with animals of all different kinds. She says she would like to be a biologist. I know deep in my heart that she has the capability to do whatever her heart desires. It may take her a little longer, but it most certainly is possible.

Kara still struggles with certain areas in her life, but it is nothing that she can't handle. From the little girl that would only say, "Spiderman can too," to now carrying on full conversations, reading, writing, and even playing Tiny Tim on stage in front of a crowd, she has grown remarkably in the last couple of years. I know she will continue with her success and make her life exactly what she would like it to be.

As a family we have faced and overcome many different challenges, and it always works out for the best, somehow. It comes down to simply never giving up or giving in to something that seems impossible. A positive outlook on life can bring about positive outcomes. Autism is simply a word, not who the individual is. It is just a part of who they are. I have a daughter with autism, and I am proud to call her mine: Kara Janet Lee.

Laura Hamlyn was born in Churchill Falls, Labrador, and spent many years in Labrador City after finishing high school. Today she lives with her family in Corner Brook, Newfoundland.

Sensory Processing in the Life of a Child with Autism: What's a Parent to Do?

by Roseanne Hickey-Hatchett

Roseanne Hickey-Hatchett, M.A., OTR, LPC is a teacher, an occupational therapist, and a counsellor. Her teaching experience has been at the elementary, high school, and university levels. She has provided workshops on human development, well-being, parenting, stress management, and sensory processing in both the US and Canada. She is a guest lecturer at various universities and has taught professional education at Washtenaw Community College. Hickey-Hatchett is a volunteer facilitator for Pachamana Alliance, a global movement with a vision of a world that works for everyone: an environmentally sustainable, spiritually fulfilling, socially just human presence on this planet. She recently chartered a chapter of the Compassionate Friends in Tecumseh, Michigan, an international organization whose mission is to offer friendship, understanding, and hope to bereaved parents, grandparents, and siblings.

My professional career began as a grade four teacher in Freshwater, Newfoundland. I quickly fell in love with my students and wanted to do my best to further their knowledge. Each Monday morning began with an accounting of weekend adventures. There was always great and mischievous banter that accompanied those stories. In the midst of this exuberance there sat a quiet boy, always punctual, nicely dressed, and attentive. He had piercing blue eyes and a head full of tousled blond curls. My awareness that he did not engage with other children in the classroom caused me to wonder about activity choices during recess. Observation on the playground resulted in a similar picture, a young boy alone. He did not play, and he was not invited by his peers to join their rollicking, boisterous games.

This lack of play in a child's life was bewildering to me. Equally troubling was his struggle with academic lessons. I found myself reflecting on this experience. He was a ten-year-old boy who didn't engage playfully with his peer group, and he found classroom work unmanageable. What was his true experience? How did he feel? How could I help?

So began my search for ways to become a more effective teacher. At first I stayed within the education curriculum. There were helpful techniques, but my questions were different. I kept returning to my initial question. Why was learning more difficult for some children? Was self-isolation on the playground a factor? If so, in what way?

Eventually I read an article written by A. Jean Ayres, Ph.D., OTR. As an occupational therapist, she worked with children who had a diagnosis of cerebral palsy. In her work she observed that some of her patients were experiencing challenges that were beyond the manifestations of the diagnosis. Thus the hypothesis for her practice emerged. She came to question the influence of sensory integration on behaviour and learning. Her body of knowledge, and her commitment to children, has laid the foundation for ongoing research and treatment in the theories of sensory integration, now referred to as sensory processing.

My own search had guided me to information that I could embrace. I was ready to formulate a plan for further study. I learned that the central idea of occupational therapy was to utilize an individual's interests in order to enhance performance in life occupations. For children, the primary occupations or daily activities are school, play, interaction with peers and family, and self-regulation. I had found my way. I was eager to start.

My acquisition of knowledge began at the School of Occupational Therapy in Kingston, Ontario, and I have sought and continue to seek professional development opportunities as the theory of sensory processing advances. Everything I read or heard was inspiring. My grandchildren today are both amused and awed when I tell them I am "going to school" this week.

Following graduation, my work assignment was in mental health. As children were admitted to the centre, my initial assessment always included a study of their performance as it related to principles of sensory processing. I learned that conditions such as anxiety, oppositional defiant disorder, and autism often presented with underlying manifestations in sync with those of sensory processing disorder (SPD). It was in this context that I met children with a diagnosis of autism.

Other clinical staff quickly became interested in my findings; these preliminary observations became a valued part of initial intakes. Because therapy was intensive (three to four times weekly), marked changes could be seen in a short period of time. I smile as I recall the relationship with maintenance staff. When I gave them my first unusual equipment request they were incredulous, maybe even annoyed. Soon they were asking what I wanted next. Their interest grew to offering suggestions and willingly responding to my ideas. As I explained to them the purpose of and how I would use the equipment, there was often a story of a child. Later, when I built my own clinic, one of the contractors offered a substantial discount because, he said, "I have an adult son with autism. I wish this place had been here when he was a child."

In 1997, New-found-abilities (Nfa) was founded. The mission of Nfa was to further education and awareness of sensory processing; to offer an innovative, intensive, and individualized treatment experience; to empower parents by participating in treatment sessions. Each parent is seen for ten minutes following treatment. Questions and discussion occur. Ideas are transferred from home to treatment and back to home. Parents are always encouraged to enjoy and play with their children.

The most recent Diagnostic and Statistical Manual (DSM5) has grouped descriptors under the umbrella autism spectrum disorder (ASD). As a spectrum disorder, people with autism will present with a wide variety of symptomatology, behaviours, and functional levels. Most frequently stated symptoms include impaired social interaction; impaired verbal and non-verbal communication; aberrant behaviours (repetitive and stereotypical); and impaired play skills (often absence of imaginary play). These symptoms vary along the spectrum from slight to severe. Autism crosses all ethnic and social boundaries. It occurs four times more frequently in boys than girls.

This description calls to mind the statement, "When you meet one person with autism, you have met one person with autism." Symptomatology consistent with the diagnosis of autism can vary significantly from person to person. It is further noted that one in sixty-eight children will be on the autism spectrum. Research states a high percentage of children diagnosed with autism will have symptoms of sensory processing disorder (SPD).

An occupational therapy clinic that focuses on treatment for SPD consists of a carefully prepared environment that offers rich and diverse sensory experiences. Play is the medium used in treatment. The clinic will have climbing apparatus, ball pits, and a variety of swings, along with riding and balancing equipment. In addition there will be "cozy nooks" for calming. Overall, the prevailing attitude is one of an invitation to play. Therapy is fun!

PLAY WITH ME

I tried to teach my child with books;
He gave me only troubled looks.
I tried to teach my child with words;
They passed him by oft unheard.

Despairingly I turned aside;
"How can I teach this child!" I cried.
Into my hands he put the key;
"Come," he said, "play with me."

— Anonymous

The child is very much the leader. The therapist's role is to follow this lead, utilize the child's choice, and modify that choice to achieve the "just right challenge." It is important that during each session the child internalize a feeling of success. This was illustrated by a seven-year-old boy early in treatment. I had presented a task of climbing "the mountain," a large bolster propped against a wall and leading to a tree house. There is also a ladder and a rope to assist. He stated, "I am afraid of heights." His mother, who was present, said, "No, you are not." He emphatically replied, "Yes, I am!" This exchange demonstrates how children manipulate their environments and activity choices to avoid areas of fear. With only a slight modification, this boy achieved the climb in a short time. Later, when his grandmother was present, he entered the clinic, climbed the mountain, stood there, and declared, "I'm not afraid of heights anymore!"

This pride of accomplishment influenced early therapy sessions. For some time therapy with this child was mostly "up in the air." We devised numerous obstacle courses adapted in many ways to further his sense of movement in space. It was amazing how many ways we used a shrimp net strung across the clinic!

During therapy, little verbal instruction is given. The idea is that integrated learning occurs as the child advances his plan. An example might be again at the mountain. It's clear there is interest in achieving the climb. The first few attempts are not successful. Some children will then move the mountain and climb the ladder. This is good, knowing we will be back to the mountain again soon. My goal might be to challenge motor planning on an unfamiliar surface. The child's goal is to get up to the tree house. So he climbs the ladder.

Other children will continue to struggle, unsure how to proceed. At that point a rope can be moved into the child's line of vision. If bewilderment continues, a suggestion could be given. "Sometimes we use this rope to help." With this clue, the child still needs to figure out how to use the rope. If necessary, I may provide support so that each step is maintained but not aiding the climb. This is what I mean by grading an activity. Just enough support. The just right challenge. The child's brain must do the work to integrate.

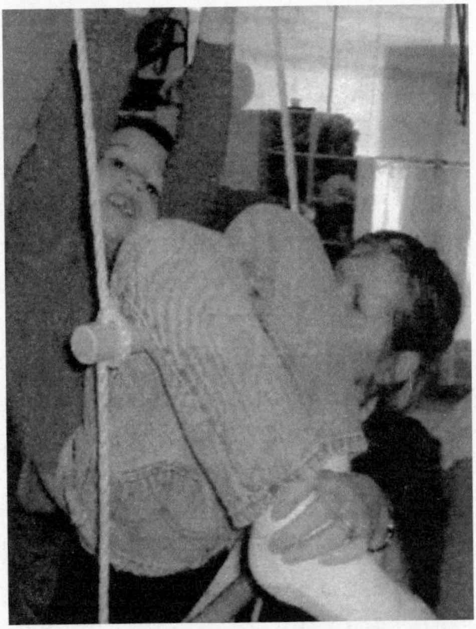

Before long, the day arrives when the child reaches from the tree house to hang from an overhead limb and crash into the pit below. This is always met with great celebration as he or she declares, "I'm doing that again!"

Children with autism often avoid eye contact. It is always enchanting to see eye contact emerge through play.

The play experience of children with autism is often impoverished. They may just line up their toys. I have watched as children wander through a play area. They may touch play equipment while passing through the environment without formulating a play approach. How can we help them access their play potential?

When children display such a response, I may engage in low-demand parallel activity within the child's vision. This activity will be chosen from an expressed area of interest. Engaging a parent or sibling with the child often brings success. These are the people who know the child best. An example of such an activity might be "the bubble swing." Here, the positioning provides pressure that is a comforting, soothing movement, as well as an opportunity for parental encouragement. I will move the swing slightly while observing the child closely and grading the activity as indicated.

Harry came to Nfa with his mom for six months. His experience is an indicator of changes that can occur in a short time. His mom wrote: "Before therapy, life with Harry was unbearable. He seemed frustrated and sad all the time. In school he kicked and hit other children and his teachers. We didn't know what to do. Then we heard about New-found-abilities. In just four months we have gotten our lives back. I talk to his teachers every day. There have been no behaviour problems in three months. Harry has learned to read. My husband, daughter and I have learned a lot from Nfa. Now we know how to comfort him and how to challenge him. We are learning ways to help him be calm and relaxed. We are all happy when Harry laughs. We are all able to smile and laugh again. Thank you."

My favourite affirmations come from the children. There are many. I met Miles when he was seven years old. During our session, I said, "Tell me what you like about school." Without hesitation he responded, "Going home." Miles received many confusing messages from his senses. He struggled with sensory-based motor dyspraxia. Six months into therapy, he arrived one day and began the session by spontaneously declaring, "I like everything about school now." Such can be the outcome when parents, teachers, and therapists respond knowingly to a child's needs.

Research such as that conducted at the Star Center in Colorado continues to advance and disperse knowledge of sensory processing and sensory processing disorder. In addition, parents are becoming strong advocates for their children. Treatment begins during the first consultation. Parents begin to look at their child through a different lens. They learn that behaviour is a message. The child is trying to express needs. Parents become "detectives" in observing behaviour and discovering helpful ways to respond. Success often comes following the shift from "top down" messages (telling the child what to do) to "bottom up" interventions (how can I help my child?). Behaviour is seen as a method of communication. How to respond effectively and empathically becomes the goal. Parents are the cornerstone for treatment success.

A well-prepared occupational therapist will look at behaviour and develop interventions that will be enhancing for the child. Activities are chosen that will bring joy into the child's world. My studies and experience have convinced me that providing sensory processing interventions will lay the foundation for children to experience greater success in meeting daily functional challenges. Julia Wilbarger, Ph.D., OTR, states each person deserves to be "joyful and jubilant." How wonderful to aspire to bringing joy into the life of a child!

The sensory system is comprised of eight senses: sight, touch, sound, taste, smell, vestibular, proprioception, interoception. Of those systems, the tactile, proprioceptive, and vestibular are thought of as the power senses. They play a foundational role and interconnect with the other systems as they wander along neural pathways.

Tactile sense (receptors located in the skin) gives information about the physical environment. The sense of touch has two components: protective and discriminative. The protective component sends information perceived as dangerous and elicits an alerting, high-guard reaction. The discriminative component gives information about the type of touch: soft, hard, wet, dry, hot, cold. It also localizes where the stimulus occurred.

Vestibular sense (receptors located in the inner ear) gives information regarding gravity, balance, equilibrium, and movement. Primarily it answers the question, "Which way is up?" It constantly provides information about head position. Thus we know where we are, if we are moving and how fast, if something in our environment is moving, or if we are both moving. It provides information about people and objects in our environment.

The proprioceptive system (receptors located in the muscles, joints, and tendons) provides messages from our muscles and joints. This system is large because we have many muscles and joints. Through stretching and compression we receive information about body shape and boundaries without needing to find them visually. As a result of movement in a variety of planes, a child learns body image, e.g., the knowledge, without visual input, that "my arm is behind my back." You see body image emerge in self-drawings.

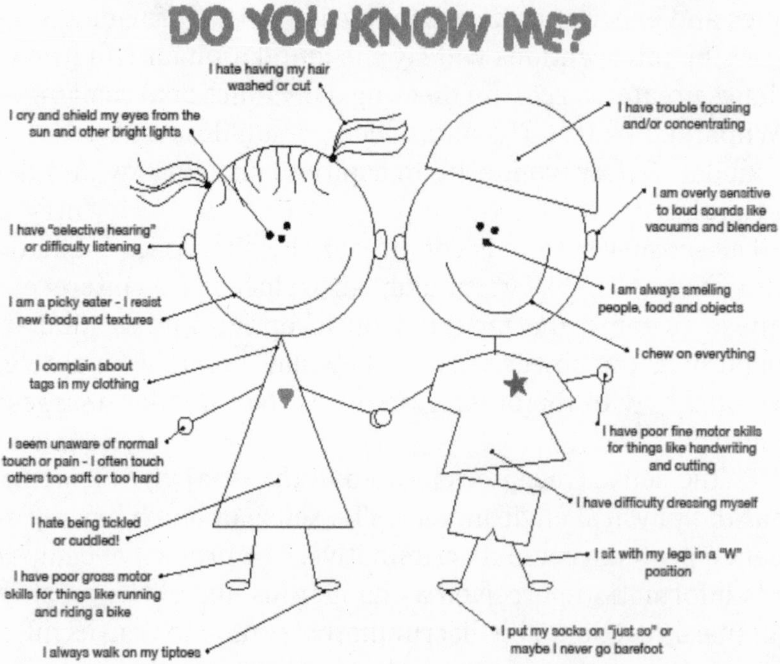

I'm a Sensational Kid!

I have Sensory Processing Disorder – SPD, for short. That means my brain can't process sensations the way other people's brains do. When my brain gets information through any of my senses – sight, smell, hearing, taste, touch, movement – it doesn't always know what to do with the information. I can become very disorganized and confused! Sometimes I over-react to all this sensory input or maybe I don't react enough. Depending on what senses are involved, I may have trouble with jobs that come naturally to other kids, even feeding myself or putting on clothes. This makes it really hard for me to function at school, in public, and even at home. I might have trouble learning or making friends, and I may have a lot of tantrums and meltdowns. I can be really shy and withdrawn from everyone, even my own mom and dad! Because I never know what's going to set off my sensory alarms, I'm often afraid of activities all the other kids enjoy. It's tough being sensational.

So do you know me? Or someone like me? Scientists say as many as 1 in 20 kids has symptoms like mine. You can do lots of things to make stuff easier. Please, be patient and understanding with kids like me. If you're my teacher or my doctor or anyone in my life, learn all you can about Sensory Processing Disorder. The Sensory Processing Disorder Foundation makes that super easy by running the biggest SPD website in the whole wide world and by putting on all sorts of cool educational events. If you're my parent, please remember there is hope and help for me in occupational therapy with a sensory integration approach.

©SPD Foundation

www.SPDFoundation.net

Bringing hope and help to sensational families everywhere

Original artwork ©2004 Melissa Zachel

Visual acuity (what we see) may be optimal, but there is another question. What do we do with what we see? That is visual processing. So it is with each of the senses. We receive information, process it, and respond. The brain is constantly receiving information from the senses both internal and external. Our response to this input is known as sensory processing. If the process is accurate to the stimulus, the response is integrating.

Sensory processing is a complex neurological process that occurs in the central nervous system. How we process that information varies based on a variety of circumstances. When we respond to these sensations in an adaptive way, we say we are integrating sensory input.

As you read this page, your phone may ring; you may hear the sound of outside traffic; people may be talking in another room; music may be playing. Messages are coming into your awareness constantly. On a typical day, you may note these messages and proceed with reading. However, if there are other circumstances that press on you—unfinished tasks, a sick child, an unexpected expense—you may find it more difficult to attend. In this way we come to understand our own fluctuating responses to sensory input.

Symptoms of SPD can be confusing, and, too often, cause observers to mistakenly think the behaviours result from noncompliance and are within the individual's control.

Sensory processing is not an either/or function. Rather, it is a continuum. When information is received through our senses and is perceived accurately, we integrate the information, and our behaviour is adaptive to time, place, and activity. It does not interfere with daily living. However, if an individual's perceptions are unclear or inaccurate, causing discomfort, fear, and/or pain, the behaviours become maladaptive. Function becomes less efficient and requires more energy than usual.

When we understand the complexity of sensory processing as "a traffic jam in the brain" (Ayres), and we want our children to be joyful, it becomes especially meaningful to seek further knowledge about SPD. Because of its pervasive impact on performance, it follows that a necessary first step is a professional consult and evaluation of puzzling behaviour. There can be numerous combinations of sensory confusion that render sensory channels inefficient and painful. How then can this be changed? Will behaviour change also? If a parent becomes constructively responsive to a child's needs expressed by frustration, what can be different? Listen to and observe the child. He is trying as hard as he can to communicate his needs.

This trail of seeking and learning will guide you to an occupational therapist.

The term occupational refers to activities that bring meaning, purpose, and joy into our lives. For children the occupations are self-regulation, play, school, and social interactions. There are many areas of occupational therapy practice, so you will want to find a therapist who has studied sensory processing theory extensively.

As I conclude writing this, I trust I have introduced you to the complex world of sensory processing theory. As research continues, the model evolves. Know at present there are identified classifications with subtypes. Although these subtypes are well defined, there are numerous combinations that can be evident for one child. A child can be under-responsive in one system while being over-responsive in another. There can be discrimination issues in one or more subtypes.

Overall, as a child attempts to meet expectations, but is bombarded by challenges he does not understand, he can experience insults to his physical, emotional, psychological, and social being.

My sister describes me as a "disciple." She is probably correct. There was once a little boy in my fourth-grade class. He required me to ask serious questions. He led me on a course of discovery. I am enjoying the trip.

Roseanne Hickey-Hatchett was born in St. John's and grew up in Freshwater, Newfoundland, with a houseful of siblings and best friends. She is closely connected to Newfoundland and visits fre-

quently. She received her teaching certificate from Memorial University of Newfoundland and graduated from the School of Occupational Therapy in Kingston, Ontario, Canada. She holds a B.S. from Eastern Michigan University in Ypsilanti, Michigan, and an M.A. in counsellor education from Siena Heights University in Adrian, Michigan. She is currently working in private practice. Roseanne lives in Ann Arbor, Michigan, and enjoys a variety of hobbies, adorable and endearing grandchildren, and the family dogs.

Asperger's Syndrome: Disability or Different Ability? "Normal" Shouldn't Be the Only Acceptable Realm

by Tom Jackman

Tom Jackman, an adult with high-functioning autism—Asperger's syndrome—holds the self-advocate seat on the board of directors of the Autism Society, Newfoundland and Labrador. He is also a member of the National Advisory Committee for Adults on the Spectrum at Autism Canada and serves as director-at-large on its board of directors. He is an advocate for acceptance of people on the autism spectrum and has been invited to speak and present at many national conferences.

After I finished high school, I went through some difficult years and began looking for the reason why. When Asperger's syndrome was finally suggested, I looked it up on the computer and agreed with this finding, and at that point I was thankful that someone had finally come to the correct conclusion. It was 1994 when Asperger's syndrome was just coming into the realm of possible diagnoses, which I guess is why I was diagnosed as an adult rather than as a child or teenager. However, knowing what I know now about Asperger's syndrome, the signs were there my whole life. I didn't receive an official diagnosis until 2005 at age twenty-nine, by which time it was a relief to know that my troubles stemmed from being on the autism spectrum. Through reading books, and the Internet, and attending conferences in recent years, I have become very informed on the subject of Asperger's. But I don't see Asperger's as a disability. I see it as a different ability.

Everyone is different. We all find different aspects of life challenging. Some people with Asperger's are uncomfortable at social functions, making "small talk," interpreting people's body language and facial expressions, and just trying to figure out what people mean when they use expressions like "It's raining cats and dogs"—or even the term "small talk." I find meeting other people with Asperger's makes accepting my diagnosis easier, as I know that there are more people like me out there. I have learned to accept my diagnosis and how to deal with the strengths and cope with the associated challenges that come along with it.

As a child I always had difficulty making friends, and I had problems in school where I was bullied, as well as difficulty getting along with my classmates. As a child I never related this to having Asperger's syndrome, since it was prior to diagnosis, but now I know that Asperger's syndrome had a role to play in it.

As a teenager I didn't have a lot of friends, either. I enjoyed navigating the world by myself, and I am still a bit of a loner today. I enjoy being social and being in social settings, but I do have problems with developing acquaintances into friendships. As a teenager, not having a peer group to support me led to loneliness, anxiety, and depression. In my case, not knowing what the problem was made it very difficult to get help.

When I don't respond or react in a way neurotypicals (people not on the autism spectrum) would expect, they look at me as if I am weird or strange, because I look "perfectly normal," whatever that is!

I rely on routines, rituals, and predictability on a daily basis to keep me in control of my life. Any sudden change to these makes it difficult to function properly, and that can lead to major anxiety issues. On a positive note, my memory ability is exceptional, as is anything that involves facts and figures.

The academic part of high school wasn't too hard, but the social part was. People with an Asperger's diagnosis have above-average intelligence, but subjects that I could read and memorize were easier than things that I had to think about. They are also skilled in fields requiring logic, memory, and creativity. I never had any special support in high school, although I used to take extra time writing tests and exams, as my brain had more information to write down when answering questions than the average student. A short answer could get the same marks as a long answer, but I preferred to write the long answer.

University was certainly different than high school. This is where things became difficult for me. I left high school and tried university and didn't do so well, as I moved away from home and lost my support system. University was also difficult because timing and organized structures were more complex, with classes all over the place rather than in one building. This is called executive functioning, which is another problem area for people with Asperger's. It was also difficult to meet people and make new friends or acquaintances. It's hard to live away from home and learn how to do things for yourself, like managing your finances, doing laundry, and using time effectively.

The adult world is a difficult place for anyone, and it is more challenging for people with autism spectrum because we have difficulties with the social interaction needed to get through common everyday situations. My university days lacked structure—both on my part and on the part of the university in general. I had the intelligence to succeed at university but lacked connections with professors and others to help guide me through the courses. It was difficult for me to go to the prof's office to ask a question—a person with ASD or Asperger's is often a little too shy to approach people with questions, so they try to manage without answers.

Some universities offer special support for people on the autism spectrum, and maybe that would have helped me at the time, had I known about it. Staff in the special disabilities office could have helped me a little more, helped guide me. I could have achieved more success with a little understanding and a little extra support, but at that time in my life I had not been diagnosed with anything.

After university, I attended a smaller community college with a small class of six people and successfully earned a business management diploma. Social interaction and school structure were much easier in a smaller social setting. People with autism spectrum need more one-on-one, and they don't often get this at university.

By regarding Asperger's as more of a difference than a disability, and by not letting it hold me back too much, I have developed into a talented and unique individual. In some situations there are advantages to having Asperger's, or even other forms of autism, compared to neurotypical adults. The ability to be intensely interested in something and the ability to keep track of seemingly unrelated facts are very useful skills to have.

One of my strongest gifts is my ability to focus my mind and to research something until I have found the answer. I participate in a monthly photo contest for a magazine, where you have to identify a picture that could have been taken anywhere across Canada, and I am rarely stumped. I use my Internet research skills and abilities to find the location and come up with the answer for the photo contest. I also handle a television camera for a TV station that covers St. John's IceCaps AHL games. I have the focus needed to follow the ice hockey players and the action during the game, and I love to research all the stats on the players from both teams.

People with Asperger's syndrome tend to be very honest and hard workers. I always do the job right the first time. I don't waste my time, or my employer's time, when I am at work. A fault I have is that I don't like to leave until everything is done, cleaned up, and put away. Sometimes that takes hours more than is expected. I find it hard to say no. People with Asperger's make great employees because they are focused and diligent. It may take a little longer to train them, as they will have lots of questions—and a mentor on the job is important—but once they know what is expected of them, they are fantastic.

Sometimes my honesty gets me into trouble, because if someone asks me, "Do you like my new dress?" and I think it's awful, I won't say, "It's lovely." I'll tell them it's ugly. This is not the best way to impress people!

Marie Curie, Albert Einstein, and Mozart, among others, had Asperger's syndrome. I'm glad that I am in such important company. Hans Asperger, who identified the syndrome, wrote, "It seems that for success in science or art, a dash of autism is essential."

Asperger's syndrome gives me an incredible eye for detail. As a child, I loved finding spelling or grammar errors in the newspaper. I am very good at "thinking outside the box" and finding solutions to problems that other people can't see. I seem to see problems from a different perspective, and it can be very helpful. I don't have emotions clouding my view of the problem. The two areas that pose the most challenge in my life with Asperger's syndrome—and I'm still working on these—are relationships and employment.

Many people with Asperger's crave acceptance and love through a romantic relationship, but few know how to actually go about finding and maintaining one. People with Asperger's love just like anyone else. A partner who learns about Asperger's and makes the necessary adjustments to cope with what's lacking and difficult in the relationship can be ensured of a fulfilling relationship. With the right kind of communication and a strong desire to make the relationship work, anything is possible. Therapy, especially with an Asperger's psychologist or other experienced mental health professional, can help both parties understand what's happening in their relationship, what's working and not working, and what can be done to improve it.

Eighty-five per cent of people with Asperger's are underemployed. It is not because of their work ethic; it stems from office politics, interviews, and the social side of work—also fear and lack of understanding of autism. If employers really look at the skill sets of the applicants, look beyond their quirky habits, mentor them, and pay them the same as any other employee with all the benefits of the positions, they would find that they would develop a very stable workplace with little turnover of staff. Instead, too often, people with disabilities are taken advantage of in the workplace.

Do the events of my life indicate a hopeless disability? Sometimes I think Asperger's syndrome is a gift and a curse at the same time. Is it an advantage to have Asperger's syndrome? Is it an insurmountable burden? Or is it a difficult balancing act between both extremes?

Let us think, for example, about the story of Dumbo. Disney's *Dumbo* may not seem to be a film that portrays disability, but its main character, Dumbo, has a deformity—extra-large ears. His big ears are not his fault. So why should he be treated differently because of them? Well, that's just the way things are, even among animals. However, when Dumbo realizes that his big ears give him the unique ability to fly, he becomes famous and popular. Is the problem of his big ears cured? No. His big ears are unchanged and are still a part of him. However, what was initially regarded as a disability is now perceived as a special ability, admired by all.

There is no disability, only different ability. You choose how to see it.

In 2013, Tom Jackman received a Queen's Diamond Jubilee Medal to recognize his volunteer work with the Autism Society, Newfoundland and Labrador for outstanding service to those with autism and their families and caregivers throughout the province.

A Gifted Son

by Dwayne LaFitte

Dwayne LaFitte was born in Labrador and grew up in the outport community of Port au Port on the west coast of Newfoundland. After high school he moved to St. John's, where he earned a Bachelor of Arts degree from Memorial University of Newfoundland. During his studies he became a passionate supporter and activist for numerous charities. He is an experienced guide, survivalist, and has a fascination with the outdoors. He has worked as an educator and researcher, and he has been employed in publishing in various capacities.

It has been over a year since my son's diagnosis, and I still fill up with emotions as I look back. Frustration, denial, guilt, despair, and anxiety are just some of the feelings I remember as I reflect on the first six years of Liam's life. The journey of being the parent of an autistic child has not been easy, but since his diagnosis, I now feel a renewed sense of hope and optimism.

Liam came into this world a healthy little boy. Developmentally, he learned to crawl and walk on schedule, learned to say "Mom" and "Dad" by the age of two, and was potty trained around the same time. He was between two and three years old when my wife and I noticed something was different. Socially, he preferred to be by himself, and he became fascinated by textures. When I look back on family vacation photos of him playing in the sand or in water, I say to myself, "How could I have missed this? I just thought he liked the beach."

Liam had mastered the alphabet by the time he was two, and he knew his numbers up to 100 by the time he was three. Shortly after that, he learned to count in multiples of two, five, ten, and so on. All of these accomplishments were very easy for him. However, voluntary speech was something completely foreign. Getting him to ask a question was very challenging. He would respond when asked something, but very infrequently would he say something spontaneously.

Shortly after his third birthday, Liam learned to read. This astounded me. How could my little boy pick up the *Bathroom Reader* on the toilet and read and pronounce every word with precision? I love baby monitors, but in Liam's case, this little piece of technology scared me to death one day. He'd gotten his hands on one of my books, *A Game of Thrones*. For anyone who is familiar with the author, George R. R. Martin, they know that all of the books in this series are enormous, and quite complex, with small print. When I heard Liam recite a complicated passage from this work, I couldn't help but become emotional and say, "My boy is brilliant."

As I write this, I wonder: if autism had been recognized as a disorder forty years ago, would I have been a candidate? I was always a shy kid and would sometimes feel awkward in social situations. I have always had difficulty making eye contact when speaking to people and often excelled in subjects such as mathematics and English. I sometimes fear that my genetics are to blame for Liam's condition.

As a parent of an only child, and someone who was "learning as they went," so to speak, I was hoping that one day Liam would break out of his shell. In addition, I was encouraged by family and friends, who also didn't recognize any warning signs. They said, "He'll talk when he's ready."

When my son was finally seen by a developmental pediatrician, the diagnosis was high-functioning autism, formally called Asperger's syndrome. The strangest thing is that when we tell people that our son is autistic, they say, "I wouldn't have known," or "No, he's not!" I'm still uncertain if people are being honest when they say this, but some professionals, such as teachers and nurses, have said the same thing.

To fully understand Liam, you have to meet him. He's a happy little boy, well-behaved and full of energy. He's also extremely intelligent and will communicate with you if you ask him a question. He's not shy, but on most occasions he will not voluntarily speak unless he has something to say. Perhaps these qualities masked all of the immediate warning signs. Because the spectrum of autism is so vast, maybe high-functioning autism is difficult to detect. I am not by any means defending the professionals who have missed this, but even now people are doubtful when we mention that our son is autistic.

When Liam was three, we asked our family physician for a referral to a speech therapist and a developmental pediatrician. Our family doctor asked why. "Why? Because he's three years old and isn't talking!"

When we were told that the waiting list was over a year long, we sought a private speech therapist until our insurance was exhausted. Again, the private speech therapist didn't see anything out of the ordinary. I am often critical of these private therapists because I am unsure if their agenda is to make money or to help the child. It is a business, after all.

Because Liam is our only child, we took him to play groups all throughout his early years, hoping that this would help him with his communication and socialization skills. We then enrolled him in daycare, again hoping that would initiate speech. It was only when Liam went in for minor surgery that a registered nurse asked me if Liam was ever tested for Asperger's. This was because, when the nurse took his blood pressure, he read back the reading to her: "It's 105 over 55." When she first mentioned Asperger's, I was livid. Who did this nurse think she was? The way it came across was blunt and forward and it took me completely off guard. However, when I composed myself a little, I opened my eyes to the possibility, and my wife and I immediately began doing some research.

When I started exploring ASD, I quickly became overwhelmed by the amount of information that was out there. What was true and what wasn't? From what I read, it appeared to me that half the population could have autism. Then I discovered the criteria, or the warning-signs checklist. It was then that I became frightened. Could the OR nurse be right? I needed to see a damn professional right away.

At that time we always knew Liam was different from most kids. As we had our suspicions, we put a plan of attack in place. After pestering the speech and language department for months, and asking our family physician to see if there was anything she could do to expedite the process, we finally got into the Janeway Children's Hospital when Liam was four and a half years old. The speech therapist immediately had concerns and put in another referral to see a developmental pediatrician. Four months before his fifth birthday, thank God, Liam got his appointment due to a cancellation.

On November 15, 2013, I was sitting across from the developmental physician when she met with Liam and me. At first she asked me some questions and observed Liam for fifteen minutes. After the consultation, she left the room and came back with a binder. Then she asked, "So, what do you think?" By observing Liam during that consultation, I could only come up with one answer. I still get a lump in my throat when I remember the words I said. "I think Liam has Asperger's," I told her. The doctor then replied, "It is all under the autism spectrum disorder now. But you are right, and I will get a team on this right away." The words coming from the doctor's mouth caused more of a shock than my own assumptions. An expert opinion made it official. We were now going to have our challenges.

After that consultation, my wife and I met with a team of specialists. The group consisted of professionals from various areas, and again they observed Liam in a controlled environment. I remember when they consulted and came back to meet with us, I secretly prayed, "I hope you are wrong." But their conclusion concurred with that of the developmental pediatrician. I still remember telling them, "Our little Liam might be wired a little differently, but I would not change him for anything."

The most remarkable aspect of this was that as soon as Liam was diagnosed, services and assistance were everywhere. We were immediately assigned a senior therapist through Eastern Health, who overwhelmed us with information on how they could help. Shortly afterwards, we found a great applied behavioural analysis (ABA) therapist, who worked with our son for twenty hours a week. Thankfully, when Liam was in kindergarten, he still received fifteen hours a week of therapy.

I don't like to do a lot of reflecting on Liam's earlier life, as what I should be concentrating on is who he is now. However, when Liam was two years old, I noticed that he became very interested in rhyme and song. Every time I read a nursery rhyme to him, I could tell that he was analyzing every word of it. I also remembered that be became very bored with books after you read them to him a few times. Around that period, I thought, *Wouldn't it be unique if I could write a book for my son, teaching him the fundamentals of counting and rhyming in a fun way?* I also went a step further, thinking, *Wouldn't it be equally special if I could, at the same time, educate him on the history and culture of our province by introducing Newfoundland and Labrador animals and landscapes?* Well, I wrote the book and Flanker Press published it. The dedication says: "For Liam, I never knew how much a parent could love a child until moment you were born." When I read this book to my son, I always begin with this dedication. It is so very true.

Reflecting on all this, I can only wonder if I could have done anything differently. Or, perhaps more importantly, could our health care system have done something? My blood still boils with animosity when I think that I took my son to our family physician dozens of times and she didn't see anything out of the ordinary. You trust your doctor, hoping that he or she can see the warning signs of certain diseases, conditions, and disorders. My family doctor missed the diagnosis and our health care system failed my son. If we had gotten into the Janeway a few months earlier, our son could have benefited from hundreds of extra hours of ABA therapy.

Liam missed out on much-needed services, and for that I will never forgive our provincial health care system. I will always be a staunch supporter of the Janeway—that hospital is amazing—but it still scares me to know that our *system* has such significant flaws. I firmly believe that physicians need to be re-educated in ASD. Although it may appear that I am pointing the finger at our family doctor, Liam had numerous visits to the Janeway emergency, and the doctors there missed it, too. How could this happen? How many more children's conditions have gone unnoticed? How many more four- and five-year-olds are waiting to see a pediatrician?

As parents, is there anything extra that we can do? Awareness and education certainly helps, but there must be more. As I write this, I know there are unborn children who will eventually be diagnosed as "special." In my situation, understanding ASD came too late for my own satisfaction. Awareness needs to be taught and ingrained into us at the earliest possible age. The statistics are frightening. It's obvious that this is now society's norm, and we must be prepared to act and adapt to it. Autism may not be as visible as other disorders, but trained professionals must be able to recognize it.

Liam is now six years old, and in this past year, his growth and personal development have been amazing. I know that he still needs to make progress, but it does provide some level of comfort knowing that my son will eventually be okay. But there are times when I would like to flick a switch in his little brain and let him be a boy. Not long ago, he nearly blew my mind when he figured out the concept of negative numbers, or integers. "Guess what, Dad? Ten minus fifteen equals minus five." At first I didn't know what to say. How could he know this? I said, "Wow, Liam! You're right. You're amazing! " I then went on to pose more complicated equations, which he figured out.

I had to stop myself. It is fun challenging my son and it's equally entertaining seeing his little mind in action, but today I am wondering if I should have spent the hour playing with his toys with him instead. He might have enjoyed it just as much. I know that I have parenting flaws, but who in their right mind would spend that much time teaching their five-year-old negative-number equations? What normal parent would do that? But that hasn't been the first time. Who teaches their young child the continents and oceans of the world when they are three? I can think of dozens of other examples of this sort of unorthodox parenting. A lot of "teaching" sprang from the fact that our boy wasn't that interested in toys when he was younger. He loved learning over playing, and I encouraged it. Perhaps I should have played with him more. Again, how could I have known how gifted my son was?

But you can't change the past or dwell on it. All you can do is learn from it. How does the saying go? Those who don't learn from the past are doomed to repeat it. Jerry Cranford of Flanker Press and the Autism Society, Newfoundland and Labrador should be commended for taking on this crusade to generate awareness for ASD and its ultimate goal to have screening put in place for all children by the time they are twenty-four months old. I really hope and pray that my contribution to this publication somehow helps them achieve this.

Last Halloween, Liam and I had a ball trick-or-treating. That day I saw him as a happy little boy knocking on doors and truly having fun. He gave one older lady a start he said, "Your house is number forty-five, but why does it say, 'Trick or Treaters Welcome' on that sign but the yellow tape says, 'Danger Do Not Cross?' That can't be possible." I'm not sure if it was the paradox of the two statements or the fact my son was reading her lawn decorations that amazed her. Either way, I'm sure Liam made a lasting impression on many houses in our neighbourhood that haunted night.

Dwayne LaFitte's career path eventually led him to the Government of Canada, where he presently works assisting youth, seniors, and the unemployed. Dwayne is the author of Over by the Harbour, *an illustrated children's book whose royalties he continues to donate to the Janeway Children's Hospital. He currently resides in Mount Pearl with his wife, Twila, and son, Liam.*

Sexual Health and Education for Folks with Autism

by Sarah MacAulay with Tricia Teeft

Sarah MacAulay is a clinical psychologist who works with children and adolescents in St. John's, Newfoundland. She has also hosted a weekly educational radio show on VOCM called The Friday Night Sex Show. *She has worked to provide sexual health education for many years, in the role of education coordinator at Planned Parenthood—Newfoundland and Labrador Sexual Health Centre, as well as through various volunteer positions and teaching posts at the University of New Brunswick and Memorial University of Newfoundland.*

Tricia Teeft is a doctoral candidate in clinical psychology at Memorial University of Newfoundland. She has trained across the developmental lifespan and has worked with diverse populations in the area of sexuality, providing education in healthy relationships and sexuality to individuals dually diagnosed with psychiatric illness and developmental delay, doing assessments and intervention for individuals convicted of sexual offences, and providing outpatient-based treatment for adults with sexual and gender concerns.

My story about autism is personal as well as professional. Temple Grandin and my interest in autism led me into my profession: psychology. Moreover, my interest in providing effective, accurate sexual health education is especially geared toward effective programming for people with different developmental trajectories. Given how confusing and contradictory sex roles and relationships can be, I think it is particularly important to present frank, accurate information along with practical skills to individuals who already encounter challenges in understanding social cues and conventions, i.e., including people with features of autism.

After sharing my story, I will discuss some best practices for providing sexual education, with input from a like-minded colleague at Memorial University of Newfoundland, doctoral candidate Tricia Teeft. As I will acknowledge, there is often a discomfort and embarrassment that comes with issues of masturbation, non-heterosexual relationships, and gender identity and expression. It is my hope that my points provide some insight and ideas on this sometimes tricky, always important topic that affects everybody at multiple points in our lives.

My Affinity for Temple Grandin's "Anthropology"

As a young person, I was very shy. Social nuances were maybe no more confusing to me than to most other children, but I was sensitive and frustrated that adults seemed to decode and negotiate social cues so easily! A few seasons with a theatre group gave me more than confidence. It taught me to recognize, then mimic, and eventually master specific components of human interaction and non-verbal cues. You might say that actors are junior anthropologists of general human emotion and interaction, let alone comedy and tragedy, on stage. (Coincidentally, I am thrilled that "The Social Players" now exists in Newfoundland and Labrador, providing theatre-based social-skills training to youth with autism—what a great opportunity!) I spent hours practising acting exercises. Facial expressions, gestures, and displays of emotion fascinated me, and

I imagine this was my early foray into social skills awareness. Now, while working as a clinical psychologist (R. Psyc.), I regularly focus on social skill development.

Through high school I worked with youth with special needs, which included difficulty making sense of social cues and conventions. It was here that I first confronted the challenge of explaining social norms that didn't always make sense or seem fair, such as those about gender roles, romantic relationships, and sexuality. After my first year of university, I found myself in a somewhat tedious summer job in a small tourist town. Two things happened that summer. I discovered Dr. Temple Grandin, and I also discovered a woman named Donna Williams, who wrote *Nobody Nowhere*, and later, *Somebody Somewhere*. The perspective of a brilliant person with autism was just fascinating and offered so much more to my understanding of the human experience. The second thing that happened that summer was that I promised myself only to take jobs and pursue a career that inspired me. So, that summer, I left a note in the mailbox of the local clinical/marital psychologist, promising to provide chocolate chip cookies in exchange for a conversation about his work. I guess my cookies were good enough (or my tenacity alarming enough) that he made time to speak with me, and that conversation had me hooked.

Temple Grandin's own phrase, "an anthropologist on Mars," became the title of an Oliver Sacks series of neuropsychological case studies. That phrase continues to influence my understanding of a person's experience trying to make sense of neurotypical social norms. Navigating the complex web of unspoken rules comes naturally for some but is particularly puzzling and frustrating for someone living with autism!

I taught university classes in human sexuality, and later worked as education coordinator at Planned Parenthood—Newfoundland and Labrador Sexual Health Centre. My work with young students across the province strengthened my determination to ensure that *everyone* got access to accurate sexual health education and information. The students with features of autism often had very different questions about sex and responded differently from other children. I saw how children, adolescents, and adults alike struggled in their own identity development, often excluded from discussions about gender and sexuality. This missing information created greater gaps in social functioning and relationships, leading to increased feelings of isolation from others. I vowed that this was not a group that would be left out of the conversation any more.

In an interesting twist, this interest I had in Temple Grandin and her work served to create a connection between three of the most different people you could ever meet. Me, with my immersion in the science of human behaviour and the art of therapy, my father, a large animal veterinarian in Nova Scotia who also raises beef cattle and is quite familiar with slaughterhouses and animal management, and my uncle, an engineer whose work has led him to assess, design, and invent novel systems and machines to increase productivity. Some of my earliest memories of my uncle include Rube Goldberg–like contraptions: the bicycle wheel with sand shovels that directed water down a chute, as well as his amazing blueberry-cleaning conveyor-belt machine for use after blueberry raking.

My father, my uncle, and I might have been seen as coming from different planets; yet, we connected instantly over Temple Grandin's local lecture on animal management at the Nova Scotia Agricultural College. My father already knew about her. Apparently, it was relevant to my uncle, as well! Temple Grandin synthesized her expertise in animal behaviour with an ability to design efficient and humane systems, while also communicating how her life and work were impacted by autism. That appealed to all of us. That Christmas, we three deliberated over who most deserved the Christmas gift (addressed to my father but still very much in my possession—sorry, Dad!) of her book *Animals in Translation*. Our respect for Temple Grandin connected us.

Animals and Their Role in Helping Explain Human Sexuality

I was raised in rural Nova Scotia and exposed to large animal veterinary medicine by accompanying my father on farm calls or observing the goings-on at the veterinary hospital and surgery next door. As anyone who has spent significant time with animals will tell you, animals provide ample opportunity to ask a lot of awkward questions. I was fortunate to have parents who readily and accurately answered these questions. This helped me make sense of human sexuality, mainly because animals aren't mired in social taboos the way people are.

> Why would two steer (male cattle) mount one another in what appeared to be a mating position? Why don't all male goats or sheep attempt to mate with the females?
>
> How come farm animals aren't embarrassed to breastfeed their young in public?
>
> How come my (seven-year-old!) friends at school were sneaking looks at pornographic magazines they found under their parents' beds but were not able to talk to their parents about what they were reading or seeing?

Granted, my father had a decidedly animal-based repertoire of information, but thankfully my mother's background as a registered nurse helped mediate his comparisons of human pregnancy to the gestation cycle of a cow, or egg-laying of our hens. Both my parents answered sexuality questions frankly, and sex was not an uncommon topic at our family dinner table. I count myself fortunate to have received a healthy sexual education early in my life from wonderful role models.

I might be committing a social faux pas or breaching a taboo in admitting that I was and still am fascinated by sex, gender, and sexuality. My school friends were fearful and mystified about the whole topic. "Sex" was considered a bad word, yet it had an increasingly powerful influence in our young lives. I learned about the anatomy and function of the reproduction system. Yet, more importantly to me, things like gender, sex, and sexual orientation were normalized for me because of my exposure to the animal world and parents who answered my questions. How many of my friends had ever had a "male" cat who wound up becoming pregnant and having kittens, or rodent pets who were supposedly "female" but later had large testicles descend, making it obvious they were not female? These were obvious examples of rarely discussed but not particularly rare intersex, where the initial appearance of external genitalia don't match our expectations about internal genitalia or sex.

Indeed, we rarely discuss how one in one hundred people have bodies that differ from the standard or expected "male" or "female" body, and many of my adult friends believe there is something wrong when they don't look like the stereotype of their sex or assigned gender. And don't get me started on the enormous range of gender expression (e.g., fluidity and creativity) that I saw from the barnyard to the schoolyard every day. From my veterinarian father and nurse mother I learned that these were scientifically healthy, normal, and adaptive; yet I received mixed and sometimes dangerous and negative messages about sex from educators, peers, and in cultural representations (television, movies, and magazines) which tried to stuff us into binary and often sexist categories of "male" or "female," based on the external appearance of genitals at birth. Commercials showed me that girls played with dolls and boys played with building blocks, but I knew there had to be more complexity than this simple cultural representation.

Discrimination and Lack of Appropriate Supports to Persons with Autism

Autism spectrum disorder covers an arguably enormous range of traits and characteristics, from profound (often co-occurring with developmental or psychiatric challenges) to the exceptionally mild (such that symptoms may be undetectable to the layperson). Some people might function very well in some areas but not in others.

Or, in some cases, there can be evidence of extraordinary "savant" talents or skills, where a person functions at a level far exceeding that which is deemed necessary or indeed *typical*. My view echoes many advocates in the field: if a person is functioning adequately or more than adequately overall, it is misrepresentative to use the label of "disorder," despite the presence of traits that we might traditionally associate with autism. Diagnostic criteria agree with this view. Many people can be "on the continuum" or show some traits, without meeting all the criteria for a diagnosis.

This "continuum" idea is an important concept, because it means that every person with features of autism does not require or even benefit from the same supports or services. Yet, often there are stereotypes and related discrimination perpetuated by the label or appearance of autism. To oversimplify the issue: individuals with autism often lack access to all of the supports that they require. Many times, this is based on the assumption that sexual and gender supports are not required, wanted, or even relevant. This has major consequences. In this next section, I am going to focus only on the consequences for sexual health outcomes, and follow with what supports ought to be put in place—without discriminatory restrictions.

Why We Need to Provide Sexual Health Information and Education

Many caregivers and community members cringe at the idea of "having the talk" with *anyone*. This occurs for numerous reasons, including sheer awkwardness and anxiety. Let me be informal for a moment: I completely understand that there is a desire to "keep 'em innocent" as long as possible. We feel ill-equipped to discuss sex and potential questions outside our, um, "expertise." Maybe we hope it won't be relevant ("they'll be a virgin forever!"); therefore, why embarrass everybody? Many understandable myths and fears exist:

> If I talk about sex, it'll just put the idea in their heads. (I call this "Don't open that can of worms!" or "What they don't know can't hurt them!")
>
> They don't need to know this stuff. (Maybe we hope "out of sight, out of mind.")
>
> Sure, they'll learn all about sex in school, and anyway, school will do a better job. (Also known as "passing the buck")
>
> I'll sound like a pervert! I'll freak them out and they won't listen anyway! (Or "don't ask, don't tell")

For all these reasons and many, many more, we can be reluctant to provide accurate, timely information about sex, sexuality, their bodies, and relationships. The barriers for children with autism are even greater, despite their need for extremely frank discussions, explanations, and values-clarification, as well as explicit skills for safety and health measures. Parents need to know, too, that many sexual behaviours are normal and okay, despite maybe appearing unusual (e.g., masturbation, sensory fixation sometimes to the point of a fetish, and sometimes masturbation with an object). As long as it is not hurting the child physically, the best approach can be to limit intervention to the social, practical, and legal aspects (teaching hygiene to avoid such things as urinary tract infections, and "that's private behaviour" to prevent indecent exposure or sexual harassment). Children of all ages have sexual hormones and impulses; no amount of avoiding the sex talk will control these natural instincts, and alas, neither will avoiding the issue protect individuals from the world around them.

The harsh reality is that children and youth, unless they live alone in a cave (and without wi-fi), are showered with messages, values, norms, and expectations about sex. These messages come from people—parents, family, peers, acquaintances, medical professionals—and also media—via advertising, overt sexual messages, seemingly innocuous sources like posters in the doctor's office, a simple children's cartoon or storybook, and of course portrayals of relationships and attitudes about sex that appear online, in television shows, books and magazines, comics, movies, or videos. These messages can't be avoided, and by ignoring rather than challenging and correcting a negative stereotype, we all contribute to the problem and "send a message" by not sending a message (i.e., we communicate that it can't be that big a deal, and isn't worth addressing). These messages can be particularly problematic for people trying to understand their meaning; indeed, negative values or attitudes that might be portrayed in irony, sarcasm, or even as an artistic or dramatic portrayal, can be extremely confusing.

What We Should Teach about Sexual Education

Within the context of providing open, safe, and non-judgmental information about gender and sexual orientation, sexual education must also include basic content. The Public Health Agency of Canada summarizes this curriculum in its *Canadian Guidelines for Sexual Health Education*, 2008:

1) the scope of reproductive anatomy and function
2) healthy relationships (including topics like abuse and consent)
3) sexually transmitted infections
4) methods of avoiding unplanned pregnancy (including birth control and abstinence options)

To this end, effective sexual health programs must be:

1) accessible
2) comprehensive
3) ***inclusive of all people*** [emphasis added]
4) effective in their delivery
5) evidence-based

6) supported by good training and administration
7) continuously planned, evaluated, and updated (PHAC, 2008).

Gender and Social Norms Related to Gender and Sexual Orientation

Commonly, sexual messages from the media and society in general deal with gender and sexual orientation. Typically, gender is promoted as being strictly limited to what we sometimes call "a binary system of gender," whereby folks are divided into one of two categories: You are assumed to be "male" or "female" with nothing in between. There is very little tolerance or flexibility for gender expression that moves from "male or female" toward a colourful spectrum. Consider the boy who tries on Mom's high heels or makeup. Dad thinks it's cute when he is three years old, but decidedly less at age ten. Why? Similarly, the girl who plays soccer or hockey is "normal" as long as she wears purple or pink dresses and plays with girls when she's off the ice or field.

It can be argued that "binary gender" is simply a Western stereotype, given the numerous historical and conventional examples of more than two genders or expressions of gender characteristics. For instance, some First Nations folks are acknowledged for recognizing a person as fitting a "two-spirited" gender category (a complex concept that some argue incorporates both "male" and "female" gender attributes in different proportions). Other cultures argue that there are sixteen or even twenty different genders or gender expressions in historical and contemporary usage.

In summary, people may feel that the gender assigned to them, based on external sexual characteristics at birth, is accurate (these people might be defined as being "cis-gendered"), or they might recognize that their gender or form of gender expression is a combination of—or even distinct from that of something different than—either male or female, as with folk identifying as "hijras" in India and Pakistan, "Muxe" in southern Mexico, "Bujis" in Indonesia, and many, many others. Some of these individuals use the term "transsexual," "transgender," or "trans" to describe their sex and gender, but there are numerous other terms that are also used. The language is quickly changing and evolving as more people with non-binary genders feel safe in "coming out."

The safest strategy to avoid embarrassment for all is "don't assume anything!" If you are unsure, then ask someone what pronoun (he, she, they, zie, hir) prefer. Every individual has the right to choose their own label, if indeed they desire a label at all. An excellent resource that we recommend is *The GENDER Book*, which is available online.

Sexuality, Sexual Orientation, and the Age of Equality

Assumptions about gender tend to get mixed up with assumptions about sexual orientation or affectional preference. In Canada, same-sex marriages are recognized legally, generally, but there are still heteronormative assumptions made (relationships are viewed from a "straight" or heterosexist perspective) that individuals ("males") will be sexually attracted only to "the opposite sex" ("females"). This is beginning to change in many cases as our awareness grows about biological, social, and psychological influences on sexual orientation, but it can be argued that in most situations, people are presumed "heterosexual" and "cis-gendered" unless they take overt steps to indicate otherwise. Folks who identify as lesbian, bisexual, gay, trans, or queer (along with the many other letters signifying valid ways of identifying) have to "come out," while "straight" or heterosexual people have their sexuality automatically validated.

Why does it matter that people are presumed heterosexual and cis-gendered? In Western society, there can be harsh penalties for individuals who step outside of the gender category to which they are allotted; a nasty insult is to call a boy a girl, an insult founded on the patriarchal view that being masculine is naturally preferable. Girls are also "corrected" for behaving in ways that might be seen as being unacceptably male, despite many masculine qualities often being healthier than feminine ones (e.g., expectations of independence or autonomy, positive/confident self-esteem). At worst, some individuals who do not meet gender norms become victims of gender or sexual orientation hate crimes. The persons themselves might feel unacceptable as they are, creating internalized sexism along with feelings of self-devaluing and self-hate. These feelings can be seen as symptoms of depression, anxiety, and low self-esteem. In these ways, social assumptions of heterosexuality and cis-gender can lead to all the problems associated with discrimination, including fear, guilt, and anger turned inward as well as outward.

Ignoring the existence of non-cis-gendered and non-heterosexual characteristics or traits means we miss out on experiencing, recognizing, and celebrating the whole range of human sexuality and what that sexuality contributes to the world. "Tolerance" of the full range of our sexuality is not enough; anyone might "tolerate" a mosquito in the tent while camping, but the real benefits come when society both accepts and celebrates differences. Folks with autism are in a unique position, in that they do not readily decode and process social norms and cues the way that neurotypical people tend to. Thus, the concepts of binary gender, gender norms, and indeed heteronormativity are learned concepts. As such, it is important that educators promote positive and healthy social norms related to these concepts, while also discussing how some related social norms might be normative or common but nonetheless harmful or even illegal. Decisions must be made with care, regarding which social norms a person chooses.

Adapting Sexual Health Programming for Folks with Autism

We may assume that sexual health information and education is simply not relevant, necessary, or desirable—particularly in the instance of working with an individual with numerous pervasive needs. Yet, sexual health programming is necessary for psychological and physical health as well as safety. Autism, regardless of severity, does not turn someone into a non-sexual being, without sexual arousal or desire (e.g., desire to masturbate and have sex, just as people without autism desire to masturbate and have sex). Similarly, they are not immune to unwanted sexual experiences. In fact, they may be more vulnerable to victimization, especially if they lack sex education and do not recognize sexual overtures or "luring." Furthermore, folks with autism experience puberty and maturation/development of the sexual reproduction system and all that goes with that (e.g., menstrual periods, "nocturnal emissions" or wet dreams, fertility and fertility challenges). Imagine dealing with these complexities without having had warning or education! Sexual health information is not only necessary; it is a right. Nonetheless, the way it is presented may need to be adjusted depending on an individual's specific learning needs.

Despite all this, one Scottish study found that mothers of children with intellectual disabilities, compared to mothers of children without intellectual disabilities, expressed more concern about sexual vulnerability, spoke about fewer sexual topics, and began those discussions when the children were older (Pownall, Jahoda, & Hastings, 2012). Although that study is not specific to folk with autism but instead looks at those "with intellectual delays" (this excludes approximately 25% of people with autism), the findings might indicate a general hesitancy on some parents' parts to discuss sex. Anecdotally, both authors of this chapter note this phenomenon being true of numerous families of children with features of autism, as well as for support-givers, which is the opposite pattern from what we argue is necessary: namely, coverage of a greater range of sexual topics (such as more specific discussion of social norms and cues), and beginning the discussions earlier and repeating them consistently to reinforce the messages.

How We Should Teach Sexual Education

As suggested, in addition to the information that is provided to typically developing individuals, special consideration or additions may be necessary. Information must be:

1) accurate (without cute stories about storks)
2) presented early on (in the elementary years)
3) presented continually
4) presented in a manner the person understands (with repetition and simplification, at a concrete level, with real-world examples)

This helps the individual make the most informed decisions possible to maximize safety. It can help to assess for understanding as well as to encourage motivation for applying what is learned. After all, as Cheng and Udry observed in one study (2003), 24% of boys and 8% of girls with developmental disabilities (including some people with autism) have had sexual intercourse at least once by age sixteen. Take a minute to reread that sentence and let it sink in. Physical and psychological safety requires that, among other things, these inevitable sexual experiences occur in the safest possible situation (e.g., by practising safer sex to avoid infections or pregnancy, by engaging in non-injurious sexual behaviours, and ideally to avoid unwanted sexual contact).

Safer Sex

Practising safer sex requires access to condoms as well as possible birth control (any prescriptions should be carefully monitored to not interact or interfere with any other existing medications or conditions). For some folks requiring birth control, it might be best to choose a method that can be administered once a week, once a month, or even inserted and left in place up to five years, e.g., an intrauterine device. If a person does not have money to purchase these things, or control over one's health care or medical card, or means to go to a store or pharmacy and purchase necessary items, then condoms and birth control should be made readily available without cost. It is better to be prepared than to be sorry! Also, proper usage needs to be demonstrated and practised. Although this might be uncomfortable for a caregiver, it is nonetheless important.

Assisted Decision-Making

Decisions about sexual activity require careful consideration. Decision-making steps can be learned. One simple description of decision-making involves demonstrating, practising, and helping an individual create a "non-negotiables" list, and role play the discussion they might have with a partner. It may be useful to talk about and write down both partners' values and "non-negotiables," such as:

There will be no sexual touching or activity:

— if one of us does not want it
— if doing so goes against the values of one of us
— if we are not in a committed relationship
— if one of us is under the influence of a substance
— if we do not have a condom
— if we have not both been screened recently for sexually transmitted infections

Additionally, there might be a "criterion" or a "pros and cons" list if a person's non-negotiables are met, but they are uncertain of a "good" choice for them. Numerous examples and worksheets for practising and completing decision-making are available online, and I encourage people to find whatever is the best fit for themselves! Additionally, the "mode" of decision-making can be important; some people might be more visual learners, and besides using a list, pictures or images might also help remind a person of the important determinants in their own decision-making.

Victimization and Vulnerability

A second reason to prioritize sexual education is that some folks with autism might be especially vulnerable to sexual abuse and exploitation by others. Others might have ill-intentions and take advantage of certain situations, or abuse relationships where a person has more power over the person with autism. Social isolation and opportunism can also be a challenge (e.g., a person with autism might not communicate an occurrence to another person, or might misunderstand the situation such that it is not identified as problematic, or the victim might blame themself).

A Case Example Regarding Consent

One of the authors worked with "Jackson," who was victimized by a peer, "Alex," both of whom had a diagnosis of autism. After several years of friendship, Alex developed a sexual interest in Jackson, but they had never discussed sexual orientation before. Alex had difficulty talking about his feelings, so instead skipped the talking and simply made physical advances toward Jackson. Jackson, however, struggled in his social interactions and also struggled with boundaries. Thus, he felt uncomfortable and did not disclose what he did not define as "abuse." Instead, he began showing symptoms of depression (lack of sleep, loss of appetite, loss of interest in activities). At this point, we worked on distinguishing features of friendship versus a relationship, issues of boundaries, and communicating assertiveness. Eventually, Jackson was able to feel more trusting in friendships again, and confident in the distinction between friends and more-than-friends.

With this in mind, everybody should be taught some autonomy, self-protection skills, and be empowered to say "no" assertively and confidently, to avoid potential guilt and shame (e.g., to have the right to say "no," to leave an unsafe or threatening situation, to call for help, etc., with the caveat that we need to avoid victim-blaming in the instance that something unwanted occurs!). A basic important concept that can be taught at a very young age is that of "good touch" or "bad touch," simply defined as any consensual versus non-consensual touching of an individual's body. For younger people and those who choose to remain abstinent, "good touch" could be easily defined as consensual touch outside or beyond "the swimsuit area," while "bad touch" could be easily defined as non-consensual touch, or touch inside "the swimsuit area." Depending on verbal ability and comprehension, some people with autism might find it particularly beneficial to have these concepts displayed visually, e.g., with a poster or drawing of the human anatomy, and distinction made between "private" or "swimsuit" areas. However, "good touch" might include areas inside the "swimsuit area" so long as that touch is consensual and consent assumes that a person is capable of giving consent. Let's review what consent is all about.

The Word of the Law

Sexual consent in Canada requires three things:

> 1) A person must be at least a certain age—generally sixteen.
> 2) This age is increased to eighteen if the sexual partner is potentially exploiting the first person, e.g., for prostitution, or if that sexual partner is in a relationship of trust, authority, or dependence (e.g., a team coach, home provider).
> 3) Additionally, the law protects a person with mental or physical disabilities, regardless of age, so that they must be cognitively capable of providing consent.

For more information about Canada's consent laws, please review Canada's Department of Justice web pages about age of consent and also about sexual exploitation.

Giving Sexual Behaviour a Context

Folks with features of autism in particular might have difficulties making sense of social expectations (sometimes called "social norms") which can lead to embarrassment or risks. Recall the earlier example of Jackson and Alex: what began as a well-intentioned sexual interest ended up having a negative effect on Jackson. An example of a social norm for sexuality includes "masturbation in public is taboo." Just like everyone else, folks with autism benefit from discussion about safe and appropriate masturbation, including acceptable locations and strategies for hygienic cleanup. Another topic of common discussion is related to public expression (e.g., limited kissing or minimal physical touch between two people is generally okay), and might be furthermore limited to specific contexts (e.g., a dance club vs. a church or synagogue). Finally, family values need to be added into the non-judgmental presentation of information, along with a discussion about how some social norms might be appropriate, while others might not be (e.g., discussion of consent vs. some unhealthy gender norms related to sexual aggression). Just as with everybody else, but particularly for folk with autism, it is important to continue the discussion about sexual social norms throughout our lifespans.

Environment or Systemic Limitations

There are potential limitations to the enjoyment of healthy sexuality of people with autism, particularly if interactions and personal time are limited (e.g., due to specialized programming or communal housing with less privacy). Namely, people's schedules, activities, and surroundings might create barriers to sexual enjoyment or fulfillment (e.g., alone or with a partner), or a person might receive negative attention, punishment, ostracization, or messages that sexual activity is negative (e.g., gross, dirty, or bad). Community or residential care providers should make efforts to ensure that sexual behaviour such as masturbation or partner contact is discussed non-judgmentally, with clear guidelines (for example, allowing masturbation in the privacy of an individual's bedroom, or being clear that partner affection is not allowed in residence, but this does not mean that one is not allowed to date). Further, discussions around safe sex and healthy relationships should be encouraged to minimize victimization or risky behaviour. For example, if an individual feels shameful about sexual behaviour, a care provider might not realize unsafe sex (e.g., without a condom) is occurring outside the home, and thus might not be aware enough to assist with safer choices.

Moreover, some folks with autism might not receive even the minimal sexual health programming provided in the school system (e.g., in the case of an individual who might not attend a traditional school, or who might be attending alternate schools or placed in modified educational streams at school). Additionally, if a person with autism has certain concurrent challenges, like medical conditions, outside appointments resulting in missed class time, or specialized programming outside of their regular class, they might be absent from sexual health programming. In some cases, a well-intentioned teacher or presenter might exclude a person from the sexual programming in order to "protect" or reduce discomfort for that person (or for the presenter), due to the many myths associated with sex. Therefore, it is particularly important for parents and caregivers to advocate explicitly for their child to be included in any age-appropriate sexual education. Caregivers may wish to inquire about typical grade levels for sexual health curriculum, and consider this in conjunction with average age of puberty, and how material might need to be adapted. Further, parents might wish to be given a copy of educational materials in order to follow up or anticipate questions or concerns that their children might raise.

Summary

The standard format of sexual health information and education might not be adequate for everybody. In other words, two people might receive the same sexual health education, but this does not mean that they get the same or as much benefit. For instance, people might have different learning styles, reading abilities, or cognitive levels. Additionally, a person who is less socially connected might have limited social interactions to rely on for personal examples. Further, they may have minimal opportunities to verify information about the admittedly complex world of sexuality.

In summary, I reiterate that as a society, we must provide people with autism— across the entire spectrum—with effective, appropriate, and timely sexual health programming tailored to their unique needs. I refer to Di Giulio (2003), who wrote about a broad range of people, not limited to nor including all folks with autism:

> Not only does the disabled population require the same basic sexual health information and skills development opportunities as the non-disabled population, but people with physical or developmental disabilities also require information and skills related to sexuality that are specific to their disability.

This statement was written about a broad audience, and it rings true for the people we are writing this essay for. Knowledge is power, and we should seek to give ourselves and those we care for as much power as everyone else receives, regardless of their developmental history, symptoms, or diagnosis. Information gives us the autonomy, confidence, and ability to make safe, informed choices leading to a better quality of life, with opportunity to build meaning within rich and beautiful relationships—no matter what those relationships look like.

Canadian Guidelines for Sexual Health Education. Public Health Agency of Canada, published 2008, retrieved November 27, 2014 from http://www.phac-aspc.gc.ca/publicat/cgsheldnemss/refer-eng.php#Ref-21.

Cheng and Udry (2003) mentioned.

Di Giulio, G. (2003). Sexuality and People Living with Physical or Developmental Disabilities: A Review of Key Issues. *The Canadian Journal of Human Sexuality*, 12, 53-68.

Pownall,J. D., Jahoda, A., & Hastings, R. P. (2012) Sexuality and Sex Education of Adolescents with Intellectual Disability: Mothers' Attitudes, Experiences, and Support Needs. *Intellectual and Developmental Disabilities*: April 2012, Vol. 50, No. 2, pp. 140-154.

The GENDER Book. Retrieved December 4, 2014 from http://www.thegenderbook.com/creative-commons/4584103029

Sarah MacAulay is a proud recipient of "The Vagina Warrior" Award following four years of acting and directing with "The Vagina Monologues in both New Brunswick and Newfoundland and Labrador" and continues to enjoy combining theatre and film with promotion of positive sexual health education and information. She has a particular interest in gender.

Tricia Teeft's passion lies in working with people who have experienced stigma, disempowerment, and systemic barriers due to sexual/gender identity, psychological disorder, or criminal history. She works from a wellness- and strength-informed model. In her spare time, you may find Trish on her yoga mat, enjoying the local St. John's music scene, or enjoying the sunshine in Bannerman Park.

Undaunted, We Press On

by Doug McCreary

Doug McCreary graduated from McMaster University with degrees in English literature and physical education, so he has spent the past thirty-five years as a financial adviser. He and his wife, Susan, live in Hockley Valley, an hour north of Toronto—or thirty minutes if you are writing a real estate ad. Once a week he plays in the local community band, where he prides himself on being the third-best tenor sax player, pending new members.

In the fall of 2000, Susan and I were in the Canary Islands sitting around the hotel pool with two other couples. It was one of those reward trips from my business. The conversation drifted to "How are your kids?" and we mentioned that we were waiting on a confirmation of a diagnosis of autism for our youngest. His development had been typical up to about twenty months, and then his speech began to disappear.

When we got back to Canada, the diagnosis was confirmed and

a support worker from a local agency came to "do an intake" on our family. Her final question was, "What characteristic about you will be the most important in getting you through this?" We chorused, "Our sense of humour." Had we realized what it was that we were going to have to *get through*, we may not have chosen that response. We may have changed our answer to, "If we don't laugh, we'll cry."

Matthew is sixteen now and the journey has definitely not been boring. Like many profoundly challenged individuals on the spectrum, he has disrupted sleep patterns. That sounds so much tamer than our reality. Every couple of months he stays up for thirty-six hours straight, catches a nap, and does it again. During these periods we tend to look like extras in *The Walking Dead*. We survive by taking shifts. Recently, in the middle of one of these, I was on the job. It was around three in the morning of day two. He started to settle in his room. It was quiet for almost half an hour—*Oh thank you, he's finally going to sleep.* I curled up on the sofa and began to drift off—and then I heard two feet hit the floor, the click of a noise toy, and a falsetto voice . . . "Everybody Dance Now!" Game on.

Matthew was diagnosed seven trampolines ago. When your child is first diagnosed, there is a whole new vocabulary to learn. We no longer had children, they were now siblings; babysitters became caregivers; playing was now social interaction; candies weren't bribes, they were reinforcers.

Our house is like Survivor: Autism Edition—food challenges, obstacle courses, endurance events, mental exercises. Unfortunately, every night is a non-elimination round. We're stuck here, constantly looking for the Immunity Idol, waiting for the merge.

Through Matthew, we learned that "fecal smearing" was not just a term in a textbook. I'll try to be clinical rather than graphic about this. Susan met a mom who complained that occasionally her son, after using the toilet, would accidentally puncture the toilet paper and then wipe his finger on the bathroom wall, necessitating an extra cleanup of the child and the little line drawing on the wall. Our Matthew took a different approach. During a stretch that lasted about two years, he would scurry off by himself and, if left uninterrupted, he would deposit enough material to create a full-sized Jackson Pollock forgery, and he didn't always restrict himself to the wall as his canvas. You know those older-style stereo speakers where the covers have little holes for the sound to come out? Well, it turns out that they are washable. They don't work afterwards, but you can wash them.

Our middle son, Michael—twenty-three months older than Matthew—was diagnosed at age five, a year and a half after his younger brother's diagnosis. While we were glad to be able to ascribe a reason to Michael's quirkiness, Susan and I found ourselves reeling under the fact that we had two kids on the spectrum. And of course we also had Andrew, our oldest, who needed support for his development. Three kids, three very different kinds of needs, three sets of rules. We didn't have a double standard in our house . . . it was a triple standard.

At age twelve, Andrew took an interest in a local theatre program. Michael got interested in performing as well. When he was thirteen he started a stand-up comedy course and began doing shows with a local troupe. One day the MC couldn't make the show and I was recruited. I told a few stories about our life with two out of three kids on the spectrum. I got to address some of the issues that families like ours deal with.

On family

Susan and I have three kids: the youngest, Matthew, is a profoundly challenged, non-verbal, autistic boy; our middle one, Michael has Asperger's syndrome. We don't even know where the third one is.

Actually, Andrew, our oldest, is our "neurotypical" child. You know, the easy one. He went away to BC for university. He called home about a year ago and said, "Dad, we need to talk. I've got something I've got to tell you." I said, "You know I am here to support you and love you no matter what." He said, "I'm seeing a counsellor for generalized anxiety disorder, I may have

Asperger's, and I'm dropping out of school." I said, "What a relief. I thought you were going to tell me you were a vegan!"

On outings in the community

Having a child like Matthew makes any outing a potential adventure. Way too many of our stories end with ". . . and that's why we're not allowed back there anymore."

When Andrew was twelve he was assisting with a local theatre performance. This was our first outing with our brand new service dog, Riley. I felt so pleased as we walked in: three lovely children, a well-behaved beautiful yellow Lab. All eyes were on us, smiling approvingly. Our finest hour. We got seated in the front row, Mattie between Susan and I, the dog curled up on the floor. The music started—amplified by the speaker about six feet from the dog's head. Riley attempted to bolt for the nearest exit; unfortunately, he was still attached to Mattie. So after a couple of frantic moments, Susan managed to unclip the two of them and took off in hot pursuit after the dog. I settled Mattie back down and had him seated on my lap. After a few moments I get the sensation of something warm and wet. Mattie was leaking. I was wearing khakis, and I was sitting in a plastic bucket chair in a puddle. So, dripping wet, I stood up, scooped up Matthew, and walked out, head held high because we are a proud people!

The grocery store is always a fun opportunity for teachable moments, said no autism parent ever! When we enter, their janitorial staff springs into action and follows us around like a task force from the Environmental Protection Agency, cleaning up the trail of carnage left in our wake. "Cleanup in aisles three . . . four . . . seven . . . stand by." How many families can boast that they have been asked to leave the bakery department after being elbows deep in a slab cake more than once? . . . And that's why we're not allowed back there anymore.

We have been through every "do no harm" evidence-based treatment or therapy that we can find: a home-based applied behavioural analysis (ABA) program; gluten-free casein-free diet; intensive behavioural intervention (IBI) therapy; biomedical interventions; hearing integration therapy; music therapy; consultations with doctors at SickKids Hospital in Toronto, at McMaster University Hospital in Hamilton, in New York, in Los Angeles; investigations of (but no attempts at) various possible "magic bullets" that might make Matthew's life easier for him (is that the sound of a cash register I hear in the distance?).

A few years ago I had to write a summary of what our daily life looks like, to try to qualify for some additional respite funding. With two kids on the spectrum, we had been identified as a *complex special needs family*. No kidding. In a world of limited resources, the family with the worst story wins—kind of. I put together a couple of one-pagers, a sort of good news/bad news depiction of life in our world.

A Good Day

Last Friday started out as such a good day. Matthew slept through the night. I heard him get out of bed around seven and I hustled up the stairs to find him relieving himself on the floor, as is his pattern. I quickly rearranged the "floor towels" and contained the puddle. I cleaned his behind and he headed happily down the stairs to our room, where he snuggled in with Susan to get warm. I cleaned his bowel movement off the floor, washed my hands, and checked to see if his bed was dry—it was! A good start.

For the next forty minutes or so we proceeded through our morning routine: get Andrew and Michael up for showers and breakfast; play the breakfast guessing game with Matthew—will it be a toasted bagel with peanut butter with a side of bacon or a mini pizza and sweet potato fries?; and try to keep him happy and "contained" while the rest of us get organized.

"Where's Mattie?"

"He's playing with his basin in the tub."

"He sounds happy."

Suddenly, the sound of the water changes. "That sounds wrong!" I sprint up the stairs and yell, "More towels!" He had the tub taps running into his basin, all right, but he had also plugged the sink and had those taps on full blast. The changing water sound was the sink flooding onto the floor, and subsequently through the kitchen ceiling onto the table below. Fortunately, Michael had just finished breakfast and moved or the water would have been leaking directly onto his plate. A dozen towels mopped up the water (one more load of laundry to do), Mattie got locked out of the bathroom, and we stayed composed long enough to get Andrew and Michael to the bus on time.

Next, I showered and dropped Mattie off at school and Susan listened to the ceiling drip. The rest of the day was relatively uneventful: all three kids had a good day at school, we chauffeured Andrew and Michael to their evening activities, and Susan and I took turns either taking Matt for a drive (four times that night) or plopped ourselves in the beanbag chair in the bathroom doorway to watch him while he played in the tub. He took his evening meds easily and fell asleep in a nest of blankets between our bed and the wall around 9:45. As he was settling, we got his teeth brushed. Just after ten o'clock I lugged him out from behind our bed and helped him up the stairs to his room—kind of like walking a drunk home—and his day was done.

He had been happy and engaged most of the day. On balance, it was a pretty good day.

A Bad Day—One of a Series

Matthew's behaviour—and his sleep patterns—go through a series of waves of good and bad. By good, I mean he's happy and content and engaged with those around him. By bad, I mean he appears agitated, frustrated, and he may strike out at others or even hurt himself.

We were in one of those "bad" periods. He awoke at 4:00 a.m. to start the day. The prior three days it had been 5:10, 3:10, and 4:30. He had been falling asleep around 9:30 or 10:00 on those days, but we can't follow him to bed immediately because Andrew and Michael need support for their activities, too. So Susan and I weren't getting much sleep as we took turns being up with him. But this stretch wasn't quite as bad as a couple of weeks ago when he woke up Monday morning at 7:00 and did not slacken his pace until Tuesday night after 9:00 (over thirty-eight hours straight). Those episodes cost me at least one day off work and it usually takes the whole family about a week to recover.

He keeps darting outside and doing these "manic" loops, running around the back field, which is fine if there is enough daylight to see him. However, if it is dark you have to hotfoot it outside, too, in order to make sure he isn't heading over the fence into the forest. (I have nightmares thinking about that poor family in New Brunswick, whose non-verbal autistic son took off, got lost in the bush, and by the time they found him three days later, hypothermia had taken its toll and he died in hospital.)

Mattie was agitated most of the day. He couldn't seem to settle at any activity except splashing water. Finally, we turned the pump off and even drained the toilets to see if we could break the loop of splash in the bathtub, splash in the laundry tub, splash in the kitchen sink, splash in the toilet (yech!).

Mattie keeps looking for food—opening the fridge, walking away—opening a cupboard, slamming the door—grabbing us by the arm and marching us to the locked cupboard where the treats are kept—and then dismissing whatever is offered. Then he throws himself on the floor, jumping up and landing on his knees, slapping his thighs and trying to bang his head on the floor. We stop him just in time, but only because we've seen this scenario before. (Once again, Michael looks terrified, his face contorted in anguish, and he apologizes to us for not being able to do anything to help his brother. How do we respond to that? Andrew, for his part, retreats to his room, knowing there is nothing he can do.)

Finally, Mattie goes into a manic eating frenzy, jamming his mouth full of whatever food he has settled on, almost choking himself. Eventually he calms himself enough and he brings me a garment, the signal that he wants to go for a drive. We get him dressed and get into the car, and I try to find some music that he will listen to and become less agitated if not actually content. We drive for about forty minutes and arrive back home to start the cycle again.

This sequence repeats over and over all day long until he finally falls asleep around 11:00 p.m.—in our bed. Not daring to move him and risk being up all night, one of us sleeps on the couch in the living room, while the other gets the futon in the garage—for now, until he wakes up.

And then we do it all over again until this cycle stops and he sleeps through the night and wakes up happy again. Maybe then we can rest.

All of these things have been real character builders. We know first-hand what a meltdown is—and we know what real helplessness feels like when Matthew can only refocus himself by slamming his head on the floor or biting a chunk out of his forearm. Despite these intermittent volcanic eruptions, he is generally happy. To see the pure joy on his face as he jumps on the trampoline—even if he is naked and it is snowing—gives us the energy and inspiration to continue to provide for his happiness to the best of our ability. And he has a sense of humour, too, even if he can only express it in facial expressions, not words.

There is a saying that a parent is only as happy as their least happy child. Andrew is taking a "gap year" in the middle of his post-secondary studies while living in Vancouver, one of the most beautiful cities in the world. Check. Michael has just finished a cross-Canada comedy tour on behalf of various autism organizations and is about to begin his version of post-secondary studies at the Second City Training Centre in Toronto. Check. And then there is Matthew.

There is an old joke about a family with a non-verbal child. One day they are out driving and a voice pipes up from the back seat, asking, "Would you mind stopping at the park on the way home?"

Astounded, they shout, "You can talk!"

"Of course I can talk."

"But you've never spoken a word in all these ten years?"

"Well, everything's been fine up until now."

For those of us with a non-verbal child, this story speaks to a few points: that secret desire we harbour to hear them talk to us—really talk and engage verbally more than they can through non-verbal communication. Like when they are sick or frustrated and the only way they can convey their discomfort is by acting out, melting down, or resorting to self-injury. Recently our sixteen-year-old non-verbal guy has been adding a number of word approximations to his various vocalizations. Over the past few weeks I am sure that I have heard his version of "open," "go," "video," and today the extra special "Dada Dada." They are guttural pronunciations, to be sure. After I hear them, I wind up asking myself, "Did he just say . . . ?" But I'm sure that he did.

The underlying point of the joke, though, addresses a certain level of expectations that we have for our special needs kids, and how sometimes we provide them with everything to the point where we may not be giving them the chance to do or to try to do things on their own. If they can't dress themselves, we get them dressed. If they can't use a spoon or a fork, we spoon-feed them. The rationale is that it is more practical—and less messy. If you are trying to get them out the door for school in the morning, doing things for them certainly speeds up the process. Let's help them when they need it. Let's catch them being right. Let's celebrate the little victories, the ones that take place every day.

What we continue to work toward is more than just awareness—with the rate of autism diagnosis now at one in sixty-eight (let's not get all OCD and argue about the most recent number), if someone is not "aware" of autism, then perhaps they have their own cognitive challenges. In addition to awareness, we need acceptance and real inclusion, not just being tolerated and allowed to sit in the same room. We want our ASD individuals to be engaged and to be invited and encouraged to contribute. Because as parents we know that they have so much to share.

It has been proven that humour increases resilience in dealing with stress and it lowers levels of anxiety and depression. Robin Williams said that comedy is acting out optimism. At our house, we believe an optimist is someone who figures taking a step backward after taking a couple of steps forward is not a disaster; it's more like a cha-cha. While there may be some things that we have missed out on, the joys we have experienced are immeasurable. We have received support from places we could never have imagined and we've met some wonderful people that we wouldn't have otherwise. Undaunted, we press on.

Doug McCreary advocates for all three of his children, but his son Michael is the one who has chosen a field where you get applause when you finish your job.

Why the Long Face?

by Michael McCreary

Michael McCreary is a nineteen-year-old stand-up comic with over 100 performances under his belt.

When I received my official diagnosis at age five, there were no personal earth-shattering revelations. I was far too fixated on more pressing matters such as trains, dinosaurs, and long-sleeved, green T-shirts. The impact was reserved more for the people who immediately surrounded me: family, friends, teachers and the like who had the pleasure of hearing my endless stream of information regarding trains, dinosaurs, and long-sleeved, green T-shirts.

Like anyone else, my interests changed from year to year, but one thing remained the same: I talked too much. It's something I've struggled with for the majority of my young life, but not to worry. My folks had figured out a system for me. They produced for me a role that I had yet to realize would become my public persona:

"Cool Mike." Cool Mike didn't talk much. He just nodded, smiled, and listened to the other kids. Cool Mike was exhausting for me, but he got me through most of public school.

Cool Mike was not the first time I had forayed into the performing arts. From a very young age I had developed an intense fascination with pop culture and would regularly incorporate movie quotes into my speech. "Do you want to see a friend today," my Mom would ask. "Round up the usual suspects," I'd reply. By the age of eight I had become fascinated with a local theatre troupe that my brother was a part of. I watched them perform regularly and grew rather fond of the idea of talking endlessly where everyone had to listen to you.

This, as I soon learned, wasn't the case. Inadvertently, theatre had taught me social skills, in the most hands-on way possible. Improv warm-ups taught me how to gauge a situation and wait my turn to speak. Blocking a scene enabled me to read into another person's body language and not infringe on their personal space.

Coping strategies weren't the only things that I took away from theatre. It helped me establish a connection, a genuine love and caring for the people around me. I found others who were just as eccentric and adamant about performing as I was. It occurred to me that if I wanted to find my people, I couldn't sit around at school waiting for a crew to drop me a line. I had to seek out my happy place on my own time. I suppose this is what made starting over in high school that much easier. All public school cliques had been temporarily abolished. All you can count on is you and your sense of where to look. Luckily, in high school, everything is labelled.

My relationship with grade seven and eight could be best described as borderline "manic depressive." These were turbulent times where every successful outing at a school-wide talent show was counteracted with a field trip to Laser Quest that nearly left me blind, or at least with one heck of a shiner. It didn't help that my circle of friends had gradually disbanded like Pangea to the farthest reaches of Ontario, leaving me to fend for myself. Well, not really fend for myself so much as get used to talking to myself. No one seemed too interested in carrying on a conversation with me past the "Hello, how are you?" mark. I wasn't bullied, but I was definitely ostracized.

My folks, God bless 'em, took immediate notice of this and suggested I start documenting my thoughts and experiences in a journal. I was completely oblivious to the fact that this was to be my first brush with comedy. As I began writing about my day-to-day trials and tribulations, something quickly dawned on me. Why am I getting so upset about all this? This is ridiculous—laughable, even. I had deluded myself into thinking each and every moment was a waking hell. As it turns out, Hell's a lot funnier than I thought. Each night I held an impromptu comic relief in the kitchen where I'd read aloud my top ten bits of the day. Little did I know this would be my first brush with "constructive criticism." At least, that's what my mom called it. I personally called it "heckling." However, my folks did respect me enough to insult me to my face. Apparently, so did the kids at school. I and the class of '09 exchanged words (some I'm not too proud of) for a while before I gave public school a bittersweet goodbye. Still, I had some time to kill, and we weren't even into January of 2010.

Suffice to say, journaling could only do so much. I had to find a more vocal outlet. Enter comic-therapy pioneer David Granirer. My mother had just finished reading his acclaimed self-help book, *The Happy Neurotic*, and, as luck would have it, found out in the weekly paper that his workshop "Stand Up for Mental Health" was running for a three-month stint out of Guelph—only an hour's drive from home. Free therapy and comedy boot camp? Sign me up!

I showed up the first night, giddy with excitement, ready to share with others my journey of overcoming adversity and finding peace of mind through writing comedy. We sat down to introduce ourselves, round table style, and—wow—I thought social alienation was a problem. When you watch a paranoid schizophrenic get up on stage and crack wise about being beaten during his time in an institution, your problems get put into perspective. I'm not saying my issues didn't hold any validity, but these were people who had truly been through the wringer and lived to tell the tale.

After that initial greeting, my folks were worried I'd be too intimidated to return. I wasn't. I felt like I was not only being educated by my fellow stand-ups on living with mental illness, I was also witnessing a wonderfully macabre celebration of humanity for all its positives and negatives. On the drive home, I came to a realization: not just about mental illness, but about any issue. Until we can sit down and joke about it unrestrained, we haven't fixed the problem. We're never gonna make it through life if we're not allowed to laugh about it. It wasn't the worst philosophy I've ever adopted. I felt reborn, in a way, like there was something new worth fighting for.

The following week, under the cover of darkness, my father drove me to the Legion of Doom–esque facility on the hill where David held the course. I was fully rejuvenated and ready to work. He announced we would be writing our first piece of material. He started with me and asked, "What is your diagnosis?"

I told him, "Asperger's syndrome."

"What are the symptoms?" he asked.

"Not picking up on social cues and talking too much," I say.

"Has that ever gotten you into trouble?"

"Yeah, a kid told me to shut up."

"Where?"

"Bible camp."

I polished and reworked that until it became the first complete bit I ever wrote. I used it in my first show. I used it in my most recent show, and I've used it in every show in between.

I went home that week and wrote five minutes worth of material. Any environment is a good working environment as long as you have someone to bounce ideas off. In this case, my dearly devoted parents have become part of the enduring "McCreary Assembly Line" writing process. I come up with the jokes, my mom edits, my dad censors, and my older brother tells me if it's funny or not.

My social life, or lack thereof, also proved to be a never-ending gold mine of mockery and observational humour. I wasn't sure if my life had turned into a really sad comedy or a really funny drama, but either way, there was still good material.

The crew back at "Stand Up for Mental Health" also became something of a surrogate family for those late Monday nights when I was away from home. There was a certain rawness and honesty that the group had that many others that I knew lacked. But then again, most people haven't been tormented by mood swings or voices that only they can hear and feel. We performed for each other, drove each other places, hell, sometimes we even wrote a little bit for each other. Our slogan could be: "Group Therapy: Better than Being Medicated . . ."

I didn't quite know it then, but I now understand how crucial my interactions with the Monday night crew were. They didn't just help me establish a comedy persona, they reshaped my views on humanity. Regardless of who are you or what you've done, you should at least get a chance to explain yourself. Isn't that what comedy is all about: being able to justify yourself to the world without being persecuted for having an opinion?

Hamilton, Ontario
March 2010

We performed for an audience of 150. We had a lineup of ten comics in total. At this point I had around twelve minutes of material, and David and the gang wanted me to close the show. Flattered? Absolutely. Anxious? You betcha. I don't get nervous like other people do before a show. I'm not scared of flubbing a line, forgetting what I was supposed to say, or even performing in front a large audience. What I don't like is waiting for long periods of time. My nerves are set on end by having to sit quietly and wait for an hour and a half before I can finally get up and say something. I figured that patience was something you acquired with age. Standing here at nineteen years old and still unable to wait my turn, I understand that maybe I was never meant to grow up.

Anyways, after the intermission and four more comics, I took to the stage. You'd think the experience would be more alienating or even dangerous, with the comic as the gladiator and the audience as the lions. As it turns out, stand-up is the most intimate form of performing I've done. The crowd isn't waiting to applaud once you're finished. They're laughing along with you through the entire show (most of the time). Comedy is more like a conversation, granted a very one-sided one, but a conversation nonetheless. It reveals both the performer and the crowd at their most vulnerable. For those glorious twelve minutes I held the room . . . and was met with my first standing ovation after I'd finished. Honestly, it's become my anti-drug. Even if I'm only performing once a month, it'll be enough to get me through a year.

Four shows later I returned to my ordinary life. I went to my grade eight graduation, where I watched my grade seven teacher bomb hard enough to make the parent council cringe. Then I came home and waited by the phone for David Granirer to call with another opportunity to grab the mic and speak my mind, not just because I needed this, but because sometimes people need to sit down, laugh, and forget about life for a while. I believe it was Henry Wadsworth Longfellow who stated, "Music is the universal language of mankind." Well, from my experience, if music is the universal language, then I say that humour is the universal answer.

In October 2014, Michael McCreary did a cross-Canada tour performing in all ten provinces for universities and provincial autism organizations to raise funds for programs in their communities. He can be reached at www.aspiecomic.com.

The "A" Word

by Tori Oliver

Tori Oliver from Gull Island, Newfoundland and Labrador, is an eighteen-year-old woman living with high-functioning autism. For the longest time she believed that living a normal life would never become a reality. Few people understood her, nor did they see her potential as an individual. However, with her growing interest in writing she has finally found a medium through which she can truly express herself.

Imagine that you are an individual currently dealing with the hardships of living on the autism spectrum. It's difficult to stay calm and collected in this world already, let alone also having to endure the typical horror stories that are created in the minds of most people whenever the word "autistic" is even brought up into conversation. From tantrums, to repetition of words or phrases, to general unusual behaviour, the entire idea of engaging with an individual with autism seems to play out like the latest *Godzilla* movie. Some people even refer to it as the "A" word.

The "A" word. Now, what's the point of that? If there's one thing I strongly dislike, even more so than body odour, or getting cut out of line *just* when I've finally reached the counter, it's that *notorious, despicable, ferocious* act of giving such a complex disorder as autism the simple moniker of "the 'A' word." Why should the very term be placed in the direction of a taboo? How is being autistic a bad thing? Considering the fact that having the disorder is out of our control, and that most of us don't even *have* a very severe degree of autism, I believe this name should be *abolished*. Even if some of us *do* fall into the category of severe, should that automatically present people with the opportunity to kick us out to the curb, as if we're undesired waste?

Well, it shouldn't. It's not right. We are intellectual people with a broad selection of talents. If you think the human brain is complex enough as it is, I'll have you know that, as of now, the mind of the autistic individual is far beyond mortal comprehension. As impossible as it may be to look at all of us at the same time, at least take the time to acknowledge *one* autistic person in your life. He or she will be more than delighted to enlighten you on their little obsessions, as individuals with autism enjoy social interaction about the things they are interested in. Nevertheless, I have used my own interests not only to divert the public from the current view of the autistic mind, but also to give encouragement to those living with autism, along with their families, in reassurance that there is hope for those affected.

Take Albert Einstein, for example. During his childhood he was labelled as handicapped on account of being incapable of speech up to his elementary school years. His handicap led others who knew him to believe that his mind was empty, perpetually swimming underwater. However, what they didn't know was that he would eventually be considered one of the most intellectual individuals in all of human history. One may wonder, how did he achieve this honour when he was unable to communicate verbally? The answer is simple. Along with his mathematical inquiries, writing was his main form of expression, and through his written work, some of the most phenomenal thoughts and solutions ever created by one being were etched for all to see, on paper.

That's the one thing I admire about paper. Paper doesn't judge you for your troubles, your ideas, or your state of mind. Paper doesn't chuckle at you with that airy wheeze at the end, all the while pointing at you and shouting, "Ha, ha! You stink! I rock! Yeah! It's all ME!" Paper doesn't mock you because the only tan you'll be getting at the beach is in your math book. Not at all. Paper is simply there to listen. It's that supportive friend you've always wanted, but you never had, since you rarely want to leave the house because "there's *people* out there!" While I do agree that many people are using their time on Earth in rather unusual ways, there are a few diamonds in the dust, if you don't give up digging. These are people that I would indeed be glad to call "geniuses."

Speaking of geniuses, I happen to know from experience that in this generation, and many others before us, individuals with developmental disorders such as autism were more likely to get harassed by others, and therefore excluded from everyday activities. How sad. We were all created equal, right? We all have our strengths and weaknesses, don't we? So, what makes someone with a developmental problem any different, besides the obvious? We are living in the era of high-end technology, and yet people are still treating their fellow man so primitively. Nobody chose to be autistic, and we're sorry if it bothers you. What we *can* choose to be, though, is extraordinary. We may be far from ordinary people, but we refuse to let that get in our way of giving the world we live in a little something extra. And that includes change. Change in the way people think about us, and change in society's "label" of autistic people. We won't tolerate intolerance. It tends to be fuelled by small minds. However, if we stick together and deflect the hate and exclusion, we can have a big impact on the minds of many. Perhaps, with the help of perseverance and willpower, the word "normal" will no longer be normal to use, and in turn, "the 'A' word" eliminated.

On behalf of all individuals who have autism, I hereby declare that autism *does not have us.*

A graduate of Baccalieu Collegiate in Old Perlican, Tori Oliver plans to attend Memorial University of Newfoundland and pursue a major in psychology.

Carry You Me

by Nicole Parsons

Nicole Parsons was born in Gander in 1973, the fourth child of Rose and Gary Collins. She attended Jane Collins Academy in Hare Bay from kindergarten to grade eight and then William Mercer Academy in Dover, Newfoundland and Labrador, for grades nine to twelve. Nicole received a diploma in community studies from Westviking College in Stephenville, where she met her husband, Michael Parsons of Seal Cove, White Bay. She then went on to earn her degree in community studies from the University of Cape Breton in Sydney, Nova Scotia. As coordinator of the Gander Women's Centre, she discovered a passion for being a voice against injustice. For the past fifteen years, Nicole has been the program coordinator for the Dover and Area Community Family Coalition, where she oversees the operations of five Family Resource Centres.

Tap, tap, tap, tap. She sits on her bed in the dark room, her little body pressed against the headboard, arms reaching out across the wall. I watch her shadow, her hand so tiny yet so methodical, so full of purpose. Tap, tap, tap, tap on the wall. Like most nights lately, I have lost all track of time. How long has she been sitting here drumming on the wall? How much longer before she finally settles onto the bed and drifts off to sleep? How much longer do I have to lie here in silence and wonder with fear why my little girl seems so isolated, so far away from me? I touch her shoulder, rub her back, gently pull her back from the wall in an attempt to break through this nightly ritual, but she will have none of it. My touch is like an assault; she cringes as if my hand is burning her skin. Does she even realize that I am here? I know now, from experience, not to turn on the bedside lamp, as this only irritates her and causes her to abandon the bed altogether and roam around the bedroom. So I lie in the darkness and wait for her arm to drop from the wall, almost in defeat, because she doesn't want to stop. She is fighting the inevitable slumber with everything in her.

Once she has finally settled into the bed, as far away from me as possible, sleep still doesn't come easy. I sing songs to her. I am not sure if she actually likes them or not, but she doesn't protest when I do so, which I take as a positive sign. I sing "I See The Moon," "You Are My Sunshine," "You Are So Beautiful," and a lullaby my father wrote, "Baby Maggie," until her eyes grow heavy and she loses the battle.

I lie with her for a while, watching her beautiful, peaceful, porcelain face. I try not to think. My days are so busy and full of activity that I don't have time to think. My husband, Mike, and I both work full-time, he in the woods operating logging equipment for my father's company, and I as the program coordinator for the Family Resource Centres in our region. We both volunteer on local committees that have weekly meetings, too, so that, coupled with spending time with our daughter and tending to normal household duties can prove to be taxing, to say the least.

Maggie Rose was born in the fall of 2002. Our first child captivated us from the moment we laid eyes on her. We were naive, inexperienced parents who were learning as we went and trying to fit into this new parenting world.

But oh, the nights! Nighttime, I cannot escape my thoughts, cannot turn my brain off from the reality of what I know deep down to be true. I think there is something wrong. Does Maggie have autism? Is she really that different from other toddlers her age? My job provides me the opportunity to see hundreds of children engage in play-based programs and activities. Maggie has been coming to the Family Resource Centre ever since she was about a week old, so I have watched, observed, and tried not to jump to conclusions. We tell new or sensitive parents all the time not to get caught up in what their child can or cannot do based on what they see in others, because every child is different and comparisons can cause worry for nothing. But over and over my mind scans through the evidence, displaying mini-snapshots of my little girl exhibiting unusual behaviours.

She plays with toys very intently, but only concentrates on any moving parts that she can spin. She constantly lines up or stacks toys, and if another child knocks them over, instead of getting upset like most children would be, she simply moves away and starts all over again. Maggie spends all of her time there alone, she doesn't engage with the others in any way, but prefers to play by herself and usually in the corners of the room or under the table. She hasn't sat with the others for snack time with the group and has no interest in sitting on the mat for singalongs or storytime or coming to the table for a craft activity.

At home, Maggie is a very contented child who occupies herself with her toys and watching cartoons. Her favourite pastime is to simply be outside, as she loves wide-open spaces. Thankfully we have a fair-sized garden and live in a long lane in the small town of Hare Bay, where we have the freedom to walk and roam all we wish. Once Maggie is outside she has little regard for her companion, doesn't really notice that you would like to walk beside her. She runs off, and you just have to keep up with her as best you can. It is very difficult to get her to change direction and turn back, and forcing her to do so causes her great anxiety.

Maggie is terrified of the vacuum cleaner, so much so that she has to be removed from the house in order for us to use it. The hand dryers in public washrooms scare her, and she places her hands over her ears whenever she hears loud music, sirens, or chainsaws from gardens nearby as our neighbours cut up their firewood. She hasn't spoken a single word but lets us know things she wants, such as milk, by leading us by hand to the fridge. And most worrisome for me is how she seems completely unaware of the people coming and going in her life. My work often sends me out of town for two to three days for workshops or meetings. Maggie doesn't get upset when I leave, and upon my return she hardly even looks at me. I will rush in the house—"Mommy's home!"—pick her up in my arms, and spin her around with elation, yet her expression doesn't change. It's like she hasn't noticed that I had even left in the first place.

Her second birthday is tomorrow. I need to turn my brain off and get up off this bed. I have a million things to do. Mike and I agreed months ago that if we didn't see significant changes or improvements in her behaviour by the time she turned two, we would have to look into it more closely. At this point we have already taken some steps. Maggie displayed certain behaviours that caused us to be concerned around the age of twelve months. Her lack of eye contact was very evident—at first we chalked it up to being shy or just her personality. I can remember running into friends in the mall who would oooh and ahhh over her, and when she'd look away or turn her head, I would just joke and say, "She's my little diva!" or "She's shy like her dad." She was content to play alone at a very young age; Maggie could lie on a blanket or in her playpen for long periods of time with a favourite toy and just spin it or make shadows with it on the wall. Or sometimes she would just lie there and study her fingers so intently you would swear she was seeing something in them that you couldn't.

I remember being at the Family Resource Centre programs when the other moms would leave the room and cause their child to cry, some going into full-blown meltdown mode, instantly aware of their absence. Maggie never did that. At first I thought it was because she was such a happy child, a "good" baby. The other moms would praise her up, saying how lucky I was to have a baby that wasn't clingy. One day during supper, a friend dropped in and, once she saw how quiet and content Maggie was in her playpen, she said, "My, how good do you have it? I can't sit to the table without having my lap full of one of my boys. They would never stay content like that and let me eat!" Mike and I laughed and beamed at Maggie, neither of us saying our fears out loud. I pushed the panic that was rising up within me back down and tried to ignore my thoughts. Was she just quiet and laid-back, or was she disconnected from us? How could we ever figure it out when she was so young?

Later that same night, as we watched the video from her first birthday party a few days before, Mike said, "Do you think it's normal that Maggie is so quiet? Do you think she is off to herself too much?" I couldn't escape the image right in front of me on the glaring screen. A dozen kids were playing, crawling, crying, laughing, all clumped together in the one area . . . but right in the middle of the room, in the midst of all the typical birthday party chaos, Maggie lay on her back, totally engrossed with her fingers, bringing her hand in and out toward her face, sometimes watching through the corners of her eyes but never looking at the colourful balloons, or the decorations, never noticing the pile of presents on a nearby table or even that there were other children in the room.

The panic I had felt earlier at the supper table starts up again and I try to swallow it down. I stare at the screen, and we sit in silence and watch now what we didn't have time to notice at the busy party. I cannot say what I honestly think. The words are in my throat but my mouth won't allow me to form them and let them pass my lips. If I say anything out loud, then that will make it real and I won't be able to take it back. If I say that I am worried about her, that I am scared and have all these concerns, then I won't be able to control it. "She's just such a good baby, that's all. Every child is different and it's just her personality. You can't say what is normal at this age because children develop at their own rate and it's not the same for all of them. There is certainly nothing wrong with Maggie." As the words spill out, I wonder who I am trying to convince, but at 2:00 a.m., alone in the dark at my kitchen table googling autism, there is no doubt who needs the convincing.

Maggie started to walk at around fourteen months and would often rise up on her tippytoes—but I knew lots of children who did that and grew out of it. She could sit in her small chair in front of the TV and watch shows like *Tiny Planets* and *Rolie Polie Olie* so intently that when they were over she would cry, sometimes for over an hour, so we had to start recording them—but I think I read somewhere that children who could focus like this at such a young age were destined for greatness and were highly intelligent. I could rationalize some of her behaviours and come up with explanations, but there were some things that I couldn't ignore or explain away, and by the eighteen-month mark we knew we had to intercede.

Our Family Resource Centre is located in a school, and my mom or sister would sometimes bring Maggie to the programs when I had to work and would report to me how they were worn out with her constantly wanting to leave the room and roam the long hallways. Her eye contact seemed to be worsening, she wouldn't respond to her name being called, and she wouldn't turn her head toward us. To test her, we would make banging noises or drop large objects behind her, but she wouldn't flinch. Mike and I started to have conversations with other family members about our concerns and were not surprised that they shared our suspicions. My sister, Robin, was actually relieved when I finally brought it up to her as she had been feeling the same way and planned on talking to me about it soon.

We broke down and took her to our family doctor to express our concerns. I blurted out that I was afraid Maggie had autism. Mike was startled and gave me one of those what-are-you-talking-about looks. I didn't plan on saying it, but I wanted to put it out there and say it out loud to someone, because I wanted to be told that I was wrong in my thinking so that I could stop the mental anguish. It seemed as if lately it was all I thought about, the first thing in the morning and the last thing at night. I couldn't escape it. I was constantly researching autism on the Internet in private, not so much to see if Maggie had it, but to look for reasons why she didn't. Maybe, if a doctor told me I was wrong, then everything would be fine and it would all go away. However, our doctor felt that she was too young to merit diagnosis of such a condition; she was still developing, growing, changing, and would need assessments done at a later age to come to a conclusion. For now he felt that maybe there was an issue with her hearing, and we were given a specialist referral. I left without any feeling of satisfaction and was grateful that Mike didn't question me or bring up the dreaded topic of autism.

About a month later, Maggie and I were sitting in the hearing specialist's room at the hospital where she had undergone the basic tests and assessments and it appeared there was no hearing loss. One part of me was relieved to hear that, but another part of me knew full well that something else was the cause of her unresponsiveness. Maggie was lying on her back, banging her foot up against the wall, over and over. "Do you think there could be something wrong with her development in other ways?" I asked timidly, even though I didn't want to know. I could tell by how intently the specialist was watching her that he thought there were issues. I was not ready to hear his opinion, and because he was taking his time in answering me I wanted to take the question back, take the good news about her hearing with me, and bolt from the room.

"Have you thought about the possibility of autism?" The air left the room. There it was. Someone had said it out loud. Now everything had changed. A professional had said it; he could see what we saw, someone else could see it so it must be real. He was so kind, so careful. My insides started to shake, the room began to spin, and I could hear my heart beating in my head. As many times as I had said the word in my head, mulled over the idea and wondered in silence, I still wasn't ready to face it. I thought that if she was diagnosed with it I would be fine and at least then I could stop wondering and move forward to help her, but . . .

"Well, well, well . . . I don't, I don't know, really . . ." My words came out so shrill and meek. I stuttered and stammered. "Isn't she too young to tell?" I asked, pleading with him with my eyes, wanting him to say that of course she was too young, she would catch up in her development. Who did he think he was, anyway? He was just a hearing specialist; he hadn't assessed her in other ways; how could he possibly make such an assumption? I couldn't control my emotions, and the tears started to stream down my face.

"Well, yes, she is still very young," he said, and continued on about how he would make an appointment with the speech pathologist and we could go from there. I only heard his words in fragments. My mind was racing, my throat was closed off, and I didn't really know how I was going to stand up. But I did because I could not wait to get out of that room. My parents were waiting for us in the lobby, and as soon as they saw my face they knew something was wrong. "He thinks she may have autism!" I started to sob in my mom's arms. We sat and watched Maggie march around the long hallway, happy and content, oblivious to my sadness and dismay.

My parents are wonderful people, supportive and loving. Their steadfast dedication and commitment to enhancing Maggie's life proved to be something that will never cease to amaze me. All of my life they have been the voice of reason, and that day was no exception. "We will figure this out together," they said, trying to reassure me. They said all the things as parents that they are supposed to say—but they never once told me not to think it was autism. I kept waiting for them to say, "Of course it's not that. How could it be that? She's perfect!" I needed them to wash away my fear. "Well, there is no way that Maggie is autistic!" I said emphatically, feeling like a spoiled child while sandwiched between them in the lobby chairs. Why weren't they agreeing with me? Why weren't they outraged? Didn't they know I needed them to say it wasn't so? Again, the reassuring words came: "Nicole, whatever it is, my love, we will handle it together. Maggie will be just fine—Maggie is just fine."

I kept my head turned toward the window the whole way home. Maggie and I were in the back seat of my parents' car and I could barely look at her without crying. I ran into the house, into the arms of my husband, and through my sobs explained what had happened at the hearing appointment. He agreed with me, that there was no way in this world our little girl had autism, she was just a little slow to talk, and once we got her to see a speech pathologist, all would be right with the world. My parents stayed for a while, and then my brother and sister-in-law and my sister came over to join us, because I needed them to back me up on this. We sat down as a family and started to talk about Maggie and her behaviours, and I could see where they were going with the conversation, and I knew it was all out of love and concern, but it had been too much for one day. I could not listen to any more.

My father followed me from the room, and I will never forget his words or the profound impact they had on me that day. "Listen to me," he said with a sternness that I knew meant that what he was about to say was important and wouldn't soon be repeated. "Maggie is the same child now as she was this morning. And you are her mother. Whoever she is and whatever she has or will be, you cannot change or control it. But what you can control is how you choose to deal with it, and make a decision right now to stop crying, to be the parent, to stop being angry at everyone around you. We all love you and only want to help. You can accept what is and do the right thing for that child. Nobody wants her to have autism, and we don't know that she does just yet, but being in denial is not going to make it go away. We will take it one step at a time."

His words felt like bricks crushing my lungs. I wanted to run away from him and his penetrating voice. But I knew he was right. I lifted my head and started to nod. I took the first step that very moment in the middle of my kitchen. All of a sudden I realized that this wasn't the end of the world and that Dad was right, there was nothing we couldn't get through together as a family. "One step at a time," I said, and for the first time that day I felt like things were going to be okay. Later that night, Mike and I had a long-overdue conversation, admitting to each other all of our fears while giving each other the strength and courage to do whatever it would take for our daughter.

Spring arrived, and with the changing season everything felt better with the arrival of more sunlight, fresher air, and a renewed sense of spirit. We had our initial assessment with the speech pathologist, and Maggie presented a delay in language development, but because of a long waiting list, she could not begin her weekly therapy session until the fall. We had to come to terms with the fact that there was a very good chance that Maggie had autism, and not just because of what had happened months ago during her hearing test, but we had become much more attuned to seeing her for what she was and not only recognized her behaviours but recorded them, discussed them, and tried to rectify them. She was such a happy child who had fallen in love with being outside, loved music, and certainly marched to the beat of her own drum. We could clearly see her differences, but for the time being we were giving her the space she needed to develop and giving ourselves time to get our heads around the fact that we may indeed have a child with special needs and abilities. It is a lot to take in. When we talked about the possibility that Maggie might have autism, I didn't cry any more. Of course it still broke my heart and it scared me, but I was anxious to learn and access whatever help was out there.

Sleeping had become nothing less than a nightmare. Some

nights she was asleep by 9:00 p.m., waking at midnight, back to sleep by 4:00 a.m., up again at 8:00 a.m. Other nights it was a completely different combination of broken sleep. The break in routine and minimal sleep were starting to affect our lives. Mike and I struggled to keep it together while working full-time, but unfortunately our deprivation was resulting in frustration and anger, and we took it out on each other. We were snapping at each other and getting upset over little, mundane things. Some days our tag team seemed like we were working against each other.

Running water had become an obsession. Maggie could spend up to an hour letting water from the faucets run over her hands, in absolute awe of the flow and texture of it. We had also discovered that it helped to calm her down—if something upset her, we placed her near running water, and its soothing affect was magical.

Maggie didn't have a lot of hair, but whenever I tried to comb the little bit she had, she screamed. During the summer we discovered her dislike for grass—once her feet touched the blades, she ran off the lawn as if it were on fire. If she was in my arms and I dangled her over the grass, she pulled her feet up and clung on to me . . . down the road, she explained to us that combs felt like knives cutting open her head and grass was like nails piercing her feet. We enjoyed our summer filled with days at the beach, long walks, and splashing in her little kiddie pool. A new swing set in the garden brought hours of enjoyment, but we were exhausted. Maggie had to be on the go constantly and, when she was enjoying an activity, it was next to impossible to get her to leave on her own. So very quickly we got used to walking off the sand with a crying child in our arms, dragging her out of the pool, and pulling her off the swing.

Fall set in and Maggie began her weekly speech therapy sessions. We were so ready now and felt bound and determined to face whatever came head-on. We were anxiously awaiting the sound of her voice and didn't believe for a minute that she wouldn't speak. Maggie didn't share in our enthusiasm at first. She hated the small, soundproof room and tried with all her might to leave. Claudette left us with a great first impression; she was warm, friendly, unassuming, calm, and easy to talk to—everything that we had imagined she would be. Each week she engaged Maggie in play-based activities geared toward fostering her language skills, and each week we saw progress in Maggie's reactions, tolerance, and interest.

A plastic apple with a bell inside was often used as a reward or reinforcement tool, and Maggie loved it right away, but we never imagined this simple little toy would have such an impact on her until one day, after a session, my parents took Maggie to the supermarket. In the produce section, while sitting in the cart, Maggie pointed to the bright red fruit and proudly declared, "Apple!" I was sitting at my desk at work when my parents called to share the wonderful news. I shed tears, partly with relief and joy that my daughter had finally spoken, and partly because I was so disappointed I had missed this magical moment. I hung up the phone, trying to imagine how her voice sounded—and I also heard my father's voice ringing in my ears: *Maggie is going to be fine.*

Saying the word "apple" must have opened up Maggie's language floodgate, because from that day on she said a new word nearly every day and began to put together simple sentences. We were in her bedroom getting ready for her birthday party, and I was singing, "Happy birthday to you," when she turned around, put her hands on my face, and said, "Hap Birt'day, Mommy!" I thought there was no way this day could be anything but perfect. The party was *Dora the Explorer*–themed at our local fire hall. Maggie was doing great for the first little while and enjoying herself, but as the group grew larger and the noise level increased, she withdrew very quickly. She wanted out of the room and had no interest in the party whatsoever. We fought to keep her inside, and when she wasn't running toward the exit, she was in the corner wedged between the wall and a chair. We brought in a

TV from home, and only when we put on a movie that she loved would she sit at the table with the others. But once it was over, she bolted for the door as if she couldn't take being there for another second. Our hearts broke for her, and we couldn't force her to stay any longer, so while the other children ate cake and had a good time, Maggie enjoyed herself outside, throwing rocks in a nearby brook with Mike's parents, who had come from Seal Cove for the occasion. Mike and I gave each other a look that clearly said, "It's time."

Our appointment with the developmental clinic came four months later, in February 2005. Maggie was two years and four months old, and we were a little worried that they would still think she was too young to be diagnosed. We had been attending speech sessions faithfully and continued to see dramatic results in her language skills. In addition, we had been receiving biweekly visits from a behaviour management specialist through the direct home services program, which was proving helpful and informative. We also had a few sessions with an occupational therapist to work on her oral issues, so the developmental team had a variety of reports, assessments, and documentation on which to base their decision. We prayed it was enough. We firmly believed that Maggie had autism, and we were so ready to take the next step and get her more of the help she would need to thrive.

Mike asked me on the drive to the hospital, "What if they say she doesn't have it?" I honestly hadn't even considered that option. We were so sure, that to think otherwise seemed absurd to me. Would we be able to access the supports she needed without a diagnosis? Not so long ago, I had prayed that it wasn't autism, and now I could honestly say that I hoped it was, because not having a label meant we wouldn't know what was wrong or how to help her.

After a long discussion with the team members, who consisted of some familiar faces and others who were strangers—her speech pathologist, occupation therapist, a pediatrician, social worker, psychologist, behavioural management specialist (BMS) worker—

answering a million questions, and a wait that seemed like eternity, we received the outcome and our belief was validated. "From everything we've reviewed and been presented with, it is our opinion that Maggie does indeed have autism." Breathe. There it was. It had been declared. I had envisioned this moment in my mind, tried to imagine how I would feel, and anticipated that it would be very hard to hear, but in that moment I truly felt a surge of relief. We finally knew for sure. We could move forward.

The next few months were a flurry of meetings and appointments and paperwork. Family members and friends who lived close by were so supportive and helpful; I don't know what I would've done without their understanding, acceptance, and love. It took some time to fill in all our friends and relatives who lived away, and it was emotionally draining at times to have to explain things and answer so many questions, especially when we were just learning about autism ourselves and didn't quite know all the right things to say. The whole family attended an autism information session at a hotel in Gander, and I was surprised to learn that the Gander area did not have an active autism chapter or parent support group. The autism groups closest to me, in Clarenville and Grand Falls–Windsor, were both a two-hour drive away and just not feasible for me. Others that I met that night felt the same, and we committed to forming our own support group.

By April we had implemented the applied behavioural analysis (ABA) therapy program into our home. Finding a suitable home therapist proved to be a little daunting in such a small place, and I was very grateful when a lady from the neighbouring town of Gambo agreed to come work with Maggie. Kim was a mother of four and had done wonderful work with other special needs children, so we had very high hopes. Transportation was an issue, so every day one of my parents would drive the twenty-five kilometres to bring her down to our home, but it was a small price to pay for the invaluable service we received from her. Kim was not only experienced with the ABA program, but she was practical, intelligent, wise, resolute, and open-minded—exactly what we were looking for.

Mike and I accompanied Kim to a two-day orientation session in Gander to introduce us to the whole concept of applied behavioural analysis, but you cannot really grasp what it will be like until you go through it. Having someone come into your home every day at first felt so intrusive and overwhelming. Thankfully, I have a wonderful employer who was supportive of my situation; I took the first week off work so I could be there, and I can remember that first day of therapy just as if it were yesterday. Kim had taken Maggie into her playroom to introduce her to the very first activity/goal they would be working on. "Maggie, pass me the ball." Kim's voice was firm, authoritative, and strong. "Maggie, pass me the ball." I had barricaded myself into the laundry room, close enough to hear but not see. I stayed there for about fifteen minutes and listened as Kim repeated the request over and over. Maggie was not complying and wanted to do her own thing and leave the room. I could sense she was getting frustrated and upset. It took everything in me not to run into the room and save her from this torture and make it all better. But I didn't. I blocked it out, read a magazine, and told myself over and over again that this was the right thing for her. This was only the first day.

The next few days were more of the same, with Kim introducing new concepts centred around language and cognitive skills. Getting Maggie to come and stand by the table where Kim sat proved to be a task in itself. And then on the third day, still in the laundry room, I heard, "Thank you, Maggie. You passed me the ball." She did it!

I took the summer off to give my mom a break, since she was Maggie's primary caregiver, and by that time we had fallen into a comfortable routine. It was sometimes hard for Maggie to stay confined inside the house, but Kim was so versatile that she could complete the therapy just about anywhere. Trips to Gander for groceries, playground time, walking, and going to the Family Resource Centre all turned into teaching opportunities, and Maggie was showing improvements in every aspect of her development. We still attended speech therapy, and Maggie was now talking in full sentences. Her words sometimes came out like she was singing, and we worked hard on spontaneous conversations as opposed to her simply answering our questions. We would do things like turn the chairs upside down in the house to stimulate impulsive reactions.

Maggie had a unique way of twisting words around; when asked to look at the camera for a picture, she would say, "Take a look!" My father had taken her to our local Nayler's Beach one day for a little outing. When they had gone about halfway down the sand, Maggie grew tired and wanted to get up in his arms. "Carry you me," she said to her grandfather. Of course, we thought this new play on words was cute, but as time passed and Maggie used the phrase so much, it became a term that held deeper meaning for our family, kind of like our motto. When you grew weary, when you didn't think you could muster enough strength to put one foot in front of the other, when you had nothing else to give and you felt defeated, Maggie's own words would bring us through. Carry you me.

We had weekly meetings with Barb, her senior therapist, who was thrilled at her progress. Like Kim, Barb had become part of our family. We had connected with her before Maggie received the diagnosis, as she was the behavioural management specialist who came to our house. I had many conversations with her about the possibility of autism, what it actually meant for a child to have it, how parents dealt with it, the services that were available, and success stories. Barb made me see that autism didn't mean your child wouldn't live a full life, but rather a different one than you had planned. Talking with her about it made me feel less devastated, even hopeful about Maggie's future, and put a lot of my fears to rest.

During the initial meeting at our home, right after Maggie received her diagnosis, Barb sensed that I was a little overwhelmed with all the information coming at us—the house full of professionals, the jargon, the upcoming schedule for therapy and appointments, the expectations and responsibilities—and she pulled me aside and asked how I was doing. I admitted it was a lot to take in, and she said to me, "I know it's a lot, and some of it is foreign, but you will get used to it. And before long, you will be saying you cannot live without me!" We both laughed, and I was grateful for her unpretentiousness and knew that a special relationship had begun.

Kim and Maggie built an amazing alliance as well. They were like best friends, but Maggie still knew that Kim was her leader, and when it was time to work on programs, she knew Kim meant business. As a therapist, Kim was brilliant at finding a balance that worked. They would bake, sing songs, make crafts, and read stories, and through all of it therapy was being completed without Maggie even realizing it. We were overjoyed with her progress and marvelled at how the program worked so well. Maggie became more engaged, more present all the time. She began to notice things around her, and she interacted. She slowly started to focus on things like crafts and actually played *with* us instead of next to us.

For as good as she was doing with the therapy, new behaviours and dislikes were emerging all the time as well. Maggie's sleep habits were worse than ever and were starting to take a toll on us. For the most part, Mike and I took turns; one of us would lie down with her around 9:30 until she fell asleep around 11:30 while the other one tried to sleep, although more often than not this time was used for doing dishes or laundry. She normally woke around 2:00 a.m. Sometimes, movies would interest her enough to keep her on the bed, but there were nights when she got up to play in her room. Several times she made her way downstairs to the front door, wanting to go outside at 3:00 a.m. and play! We had to sit in front of the door in our front porch while she screeched and begged to go out. She would cry so hard her face would get blotchy and her voice turn hoarse.

These nights were the worst. These were the moments when we hated autism, when we asked, "Why did this happen to Maggie?" These were the times when we felt alone and isolated and like nobody else understood what we were going through. Or some night we would find ourselves driving around in the wee hours of the morning, and once she was asleep we had to sit in the car in the driveway because moving her would wake her up and then the cycle would start all over again. The one good thing about our nights was that Maggie developed a love of storybooks. I had always read to her, but she would show very little interest beyond the first few pages. Now she brings them to us—"Read book"—and enjoys three to five books each night.

Along with this came a huge increase in her physical contact. Maggie finally loved to be snuggled up in bed, arms wrapped around us, and was constantly giving hugs and kisses. For us as parents, these things were invaluable.

Maggie enjoyed playing with other children one on one but still struggled with groups. We set up play dates at our home, and she began to ask for her friends by name, which was music to our ears. Birthday parties and social events were still difficult, and it would've been so easy to decline the many invitations, but knowing that social issues are such a huge part of autism, we kept at it. One day my father dropped us off at a local hall for a party, and when Maggie saw where she was, she started crying in protest. I took a deep breath and braced myself for the struggle that would ensue.

"You don't have to take her in there," Dad said softly. I could hardly hear him through Maggie's sobbing. "Yes, I do," I said, trying to make myself sound strong, when inside I was feeling defeated even before we got out of the car. Did I have it in me today? Could I go through one more party? The last few we had been to, we only lasted about thirty minutes because Maggie cried and would not stop heading for the door. This party was no exception, but over time she began to stay longer, engage in the games, and even sit at the table. By the time her third birthday rolled around, she was the belle of the ball and was the last kid to leave, for a change!

The year she turned four we tried to introduce new things like movies and shows at the Arts and Culture Centre. The first few attempts didn't go very well, and we ended up leaving because she was so scared and overwhelmed, but before she started school we had conquered her fear of shows and she grew to love them. Her first haircut was extremely scary, and it took several visits to the hair salon to get her in the chair. The stylist was very patient and let her squirt water on the mirror while she quickly cut her bangs—

whatever works! Most of the things in her life were broken down in steps and accomplished through trial and error. It took a lot of patience, but the results were always worth it.

Maggie completed the ABA program in the spring of 2007. She had successfully reached every single goal that had been set for her, and although we could have kept going, it would have meant repeating the same programs, and we thought the break from it for the last few months before she started school would be good for her. She still lacked some social skills, but we felt confident that starting school in the fall would help in this area tremendously.

Finishing up the program was bittersweet. Of course, we were over the moon with pride for how well Maggie had done. To this day we are grateful for the remarkable work Kim did with her on a daily basis and truly believe if not for her guidance, creativity, and fortitude, Maggie would not have done as well as she had. We missed Kim, her friendship, and her daily presence in our lives, but we have managed to keep in touch through the years, and she still remains a very important person to our family. And Barb was right when she said at that very first meeting that I wouldn't know what to do without her, because once the ABA program was finished, I honestly felt nervous about not having her influence and guidance in our lives. But we were aware that, if need be, we could resume support in the home for Maggie even after she started school, so it was comforting to have that backup plan.

When Maggie started kindergarten, she was so ready. Fortunately for us, my office and the Family Resource Centre are located at her school, right next to her first classroom, so she was already accustomed to the physical environment. I was so nervous about her going on the bus, but she handled it with grace and courage, like most things in her life. Her school life has been successful. She benefits greatly from having supports in the classroom and doesn't need to come out of class except for tests sometimes. I have been very fortunate to have a supportive staff of teachers working with her and an understanding administrative team who work along with me to ensure Maggie receives the best education possible.

William Mercer Academy's team of student assistants and instructional resource teachers have become like a second family to us. They have worked with Maggie, gotten to know her quirks, and are able to anticipate things that may upset her. Over the years she has enjoyed choir and taken part in most activities available to her, like concerts and field trips.

School life hasn't always been easy, though, and it can feel like a roller coaster ride at times. Maggie has gone through phases where waking her up in the mornings resulted in screaming, refusing to get dressed, protesting all the way. Around the grade-four mark, just the daily grind of getting her in my car and into the building was like moving a mountain, but fortunately it didn't last past that age. She has had her tantrums on classroom floors, bolted herself to the stage in the gym, refused to leave the music room, left class to come to my office, argued with teachers, and declined to complete work that she is more than capable of. But we have a great rapport with open communication, and this is the key to any child's pathway in the education system.

Maggie had the unique experience of co-writing a storybook with her grandfather during grade two. *What Colour is the Ocean?* is the name of a song they wrote together, and we were thrilled to see it come to life on the page. In April 2010, the book won an Atlantic Book Award: the Lillian Shepherd Memorial Award for Excellence in Illustration. Along with her Grandy (author Gary Collins), Maggie has attended social literary functions and book launches and has spoken at festivals. She has been interviewed on TV, radio, and for newspapers. When asked by so many adoring fans when she will be a part of another book, Maggie's response is usually the same: "No, thank you. I didn't like all the fuss and attention."

Autism Camp at Maxx Simms Camp on the Exploits River has proven to be a highlight for us, and we have attended three summers in a row. Maggie loves the setting, the amenities, and activities—Mike and I love the freedom it affords us. We don't have to worry if she has a meltdown or yells; it's so relaxing to know nobody is going to stare or judge, because sometimes Maggie can certainly act out in public places when she doesn't get what she wants, when she is tired of waiting, or when plans suddenly change without warning. As a parent, I have to be twenty steps ahead of her all the time, trying to anticipate outcomes so I can be prepared.

We role play how things may turn out so Maggie can explore her feelings and won't feel blindsided should something happen that she doesn't want or isn't ready for. This can be challenging with school life sometimes. If her class is scheduled to go outside to the playground and something prohibits them from doing so at the last minute, this can cause great upset. One day at lunch when she was in grade three, I placed her food on a blue plate, and as soon as she saw it, she threw it at the wall, screaming, "I wanted the red plate!" Chicken nuggets went flying across the room, milk was spilled, and feelings hurt. "I was thinking of the red plate all morning, Mom!" she wailed. Silly me for not thinking to ask beforehand!

As I write this, it's Sunday afternoon, almost dark outside, and it's only 5:00 p.m., my favourite time of the year. We are busy as usual, rushing to make supper, do a bit of homework, answer the phone, which never stops ringing at our house, get cleaned up, and get ready to go to church on time. "Are you sure you want to go to church tonight?" I ask her for the tenth time today. "Yes, Mom, you know I don't want to miss it," she answers impatiently. "Okay, my love, just checking." I smile to myself, and for a few moments my mind wanders back to a time, not so long ago, when going to our church would have caused much anxiety for me and irritation for Maggie.

How far we have come. How many valuable lessons I have learned, not the least of which is that humour can fix almost anything and defuse most tense situations. We truly live in the moment and try to get the most of each day, each experience. We have always been a very lively family, full of spontaneity, but now we have taken that to a whole new level. A simple ride to the next town for an ice cream may lead us all the way to Clarenville to see a movie. I don't stress about having a perfectly clean house and don't let things like not having the floors mopped on Saturday stop me from a skidoo ride or going to the beach. I have learned that even though

I cannot go through a wall, I can find a way around it, and if I can't get around it, I just have to start hitting it until it falls. Being an advocate for my child is my greatest role now, and I am constantly educating and explaining, hoping to change minds, rules, and perceptions.

I know now that what others think of us is truly not my problem nor any of my business. We have gotten all the looks from other parents, the expressions of disapproval for something Maggie may be doing in Walmart, like sitting on the dirty floor reading a book or getting upset because the kids' movie rack has been moved to another section. I am so over it and keep my head high. I wish I had the energy or the inclination to tell these onlookers our situation, to explain to them that, once upon a time, I couldn't get my daughter to stay in a store or even look around at what was on the shelves. But their opinions do not affect us or matter. I have a wonderful circle of friends who listen to me, support me, and accept Maggie for who she is. Some of us parents of children with autism try to get together as often as we can to talk, laugh, vent, and problem-solve. Our autism chapter in Gander fizzled out after a few years, as not having an actual office or a paid employee proved to be difficult and the large geographical area was daunting. Lately, though, we have started to come together again and formalize a group, and I am hopeful for the future and thankful for the support from the Grand Falls office in helping us organize events.

I have learned that it's okay to build a snowman at midnight or stargaze at 3:00 a.m. It's perfectly fine to swim after dark and open presents at the beginning of the birthday party as opposed to the end. It's okay sometimes to have ice cream with breakfast and wear purple with green. Where is that rule book?

I have struggled to let go of all the what-ifs. What if I'd had a C-section? What if I hadn't had to take insulin during my pregnancy? What if I'd eaten too much tuna? (I had heard that consuming tuna was the cause of autism at one point.) What if I hadn't had induced labour? I have stopped trying to find the cause for it and decided to concentrate more on the healing.

I have learned to look at the world differently and to see things from a totally different angle. Maggie teaches me that every day. One day, while playing with her piano, she asked, "Mom, can you hear the colours?" I walked closer to her as she was playing the high notes on the keyboard. "What do you mean?" I responded. "Well, don't you think these notes up here, these high ones, sound like yellow?" I stopped and considered it. "If they sound like yellow, then what does black sound like?" I wondered out loud. "Oh, they are way down here," she said, as she started hammering on the lowest keys. "And blue and green are right in the middle." I was amazed at her perception. We spent the next fifteen minutes or so picking out different shades of keys and listening to the colours. "The piano is a rainbow, Mom! Didn't you know that?"

Maggie is now a beautiful twelve-year-old girl in grade seven. She lives a very full life where her days are consumed with school, homework, friends, school activities, Pathfinders, Youth Group, piano lessons, and more friends. So far, this year has proven to be the toughest, academically speaking, especially with math. Together with school support and nightly reviews around our dining room table, we are helping her hold her own, and recently we celebrated her induction into the eighty-plus-average club. I am a bit of an overachiever, so I have had to let go of my desire for her to have higher marks, and I tell myself daily that as long as she is doing her best and is happy, healthy, and navigating through the world of junior high as independently as possible, then we are doing all right.

Her classmates are very supportive, and every year the school staff gives me time to go into Maggie's classroom and initiate a little "powwow." We have a chat about autism in general and then get into the specifics of Maggie's unique personality and behaviours in the class. We brainstorm ways they can help and make it easier for her. It is always a very open and honest conversation. They ask questions and provide feedback in an attempt to understand her better, and I hope that their acceptance and tolerance will always be this way.

We have seen some changes in Maggie's social life. This is the age where kids turn into teenagers, abandon their toys, and become socially conscious. Maggie may not be at the level of some of her friends, but she isn't far behind. She has had the same group of friends since she was preschool age, and I feel like sometimes they know things about her and can anticipate how she will feel and react better than I can. They know her triggers, how to make her feel better, and how to protect her. I am so grateful to have such a loving bunch of girls standing by her. Adolescence is a trying time for any kid, and having autism on top of all the changes certainly makes it even more confusing.

Our home is like an open house, and her friends have grown up along with her at our kitchen table, around our Christmas tree, on holidays with us, trips to St. John's, meals, sleepovers. Maggie always has a friend in our midst, and we love it. She has become her own person with her quirks, opinions, and beliefs, with unique characteristics that make up her spirit. She loves to draw and claims that she can hear you better when she is creating on the page. She loves to bake and make tarts with her Nanny Rose and loves that she can do this better than me.

She still doesn't like to eat at the table with others, and she prefers her own table in public restaurants. She cannot handle denim, lace, zippers, straps, or buttons on her clothes. She hasn't added many new things to her diet and never tires of eating the same things over and over. She still hates to clean up her room and is awkward with housework. She still needs help rinsing the shampoo out of her hair. Fireworks and sirens still scare her, and combs and brushes still hurt her scalp.

Maggie has a vast imagination, is dramatic and lively, and loves to put off skits and magic shows. She doesn't always get jokes or sarcasm or why kids want to grow up. The volume on the car stereo has to be set at eight no matter what. She loves animals and believes they understand more than we are aware. She loves nature and gets the most out of every season. She believes snow is one of God's greatest creations and cries when it melts. Scrambled eggs are for breakfast only on Wednesday. Maggie is stubborn and indignant and has a hard time admitting when she's wrong.

She still sleeps with her teddy bear, Lotso, secretly carries him everywhere we go, and is offended if you don't consider him a part of our family. She cannot fall asleep without me or her father next to her, but refuses to share her bed with a girlfriend during sleepovers. She never drinks anything other than milk or water and doesn't chew gum. A drive around our little town has to end off each and every day, even if we have just come from a long drive.

Maggie continues to express love and expand her capacity to feel and understand empathy. Her comprehension of music and her appreciation for eclectic styles increases all the time. She still loves to splash in puddles, feel summer rain on her face, smash frozen ice puddles with her boots, roll around in the snow, and jump in colourful leaf piles, and will probably continue to do so for many years to come. Maggie loses her temper when things don't go her way, and she blurts out insults on impulse that she regrets once she has calmed down and begs for your forgiveness. She has very little patience and has a hard time when she doesn't get her own way. She struggles to take medicine, is terrified of needles, and is uncomfortable in doctors' offices. She uses computers, iPads, and cellphones as if she created them, and she dreams of having her own video on YouTube. She hates to have makeup on her face for more than five minutes, but loves to have her makeup case full.

Maggie easily makes connections with children who have disabilities. She isn't intimidated or hesitant around them and seems to have a calming effect when she talks to them. She will not put any kind of accessory or colour in her hair, and she will probably never have her ears pierced. She loves her friends unconditionally, loves spending time with them more than anything, but thinks simply hanging out is a complete waste of time when they could actually be "doing" something. Maggie loves all things Disney and imagines her future working there, creating and incorporating rides and attractions that are less scary and loud for children with autism. Her friend Alexander, who has cerebral palsy, is truly one of the great loves of her life; she doesn't see his limitations and claims to understand everything he says to her because they have their own language.

Maggie is generous and loves to give to charity. She is honest to a fault, and if you find her opinion offensive, then she doesn't understand why you asked for it in the first place. She claims to enjoy being an only child but often wonders what life would be like with a sibling. She thinks she has the coolest aunts and uncles and loves the fact that she has a lot of cousins but wishes they all lived closer. She worships her grandparents and cannot imagine them growing old or not being exactly what they are now, and she simply refuses to entertain the idea that someday they won't be there.

Maggie firmly believes that if you love someone enough, there is no way they can die, and that if by some chance I leave this earth before she does, she is simply coming with me because we can never be apart. She thinks her father is the strongest man that ever walked, he can make anything with his hands and fix any problem she will ever have. Maggie's opinion of me is so high that I struggle to live up to it each and every day.

Can all her little idiosyncrasies be attributed to autism? We will never truly know, and we have to come to accept that as part of her mystery. What we do know is that the autistic mind is, with absolute certainty, fascinating, brilliant, confusing, and compelling. Are there things I would change about my daughter if I could? Of course. Do I wish every single day that she didn't have autism? You bet. But I have learned that when we become fixated on trying to change our children, or fix their problems, we lose sight of the positive, the good stuff. We need to spend our time and energy enhancing and celebrating their natural talents. Instead of trying to make Maggie bend and fit into the world around her, we are helping to mould and shape the world to fit her.

It isn't easy. Every day is a struggle and presents new challenges, but for our little family, the good days outweigh the bad, the positive outshines the negative. It's Maggie's world, after all—we just live in it! And what a beautiful place it is: it's not what I thought it would be, these roads we are journeying on are not in our original road map, our destination may not be where I thought we would end up, but for now we are embracing the detours along the way and trying to find the beauty in each and every one. And you know what? Maggie will be just fine. And just maybe, somewhere along the way, we may have to "carry you me."

Nicole and Michael Parsons have made a home in Hare Bay, Newfoundland and Labrador, where Nicole is very involved with her community and serves on a variety of committees. She has a passion for animals, an intolerance for animal cruelty, and does volunteer work for the SPCA. She loves to write and wishes she had more time to cultivate her skills. Music is a big part of her life as well, and she enjoys singing, sometimes for public functions but more often for the simple pleasures of kitchen parties. Nicole's greatest love is her daughter Maggie, her most important role is being a mother, and she is committed to being Maggie's advocate and cheerleader.

It Takes a Community to Raise a Child

by Bridget Ricketts

Bridget Ricketts was born in St. John's, Newfoundland and Labrador, and grew up in Marystown on the beautiful Burin Peninsula. When she was ten years old, her parents bought a restaurant on the Trans-Canada Highway near Glovertown, where Bridget worked as a waitress, cashier, and short-order cook during her teenaged years. She fell in love with school at Glovertown Regional High, and several years later she realized that education was her calling.

It is said that it takes a community to raise a child. For my son, Andrew, the support and skills that made him the bright young man he is today came from doctors, pediatricians, and therapists, but more importantly the love and attention from his own family. Let me tell you our story.

I had to talk my husband into having a second child. Our daughter, Katie, was two years old when I arranged for my parents to babysit, and we went out to Fog City for dinner. Before our meal arrived I launched into my prepared speech. My reasons were simple: we were good parents, we could provide a good home, and, most importantly, our daughter would have a brother or sister to grow up with. I think it was this last point that struck home for him, as we both have siblings and we couldn't imagine what it would be like to grow up an only child.

My husband reached across the table and took my hand. Yes, he agreed. Let's have another baby.

After that it didn't take long before I was pregnant. On the evening my grandfather passed away at the Department of Veteran Affairs Pavilion, I took a pregnancy test. My husband and daughter were out in front of our house playing ball in the cul-de-sac. I showed him the little stick with the two stripes, and together we sat on the step in the afternoon sun and marvelled at the new life we had started that would be part of our family.

Later that evening I visited my grandfather for the last time and whispered in his ear that I had a little baby growing inside me. He wasn't conscious and the end was near, but his eyes flickered as I whispered our secret. I didn't tell my family until after the funeral, and the news resounded with everyone that, indeed, life does come full circle.

I had a good pregnancy and grew round with what everyone thought would be another girl. My husband kept referring to the baby as Emily. I never said anything, as for some reason I knew it was a boy. I was due on Valentine's Day, but on January 26, after reciting the *Elmo in Grouchland* story to Katie for the two hundredth time, I fell asleep next to her. At eight thirty I woke to a gush of water between my legs and waddled out to find my husband, who was reading. He proudly said, "I told you today was the day!" Sure enough, that morning he had indeed said that.

Things went much faster the second time around, and at 2:06 a.m., with barely a chance to get my feet in the stirrups, our little baby was born. I remember the doctor saying it was a boy, and I was surprised that I had completely forgotten to care about whether it was a boy or girl! It took us three days to name him, but finally we settled on Andrew, and one of his middle names was Maxwell, my grandfather's name.

Andrew was a great baby. Unlike his sister, who took five days to learn how to latch on, Andrew was a breastfeeding champ! However, we were soon to find out he was not as flexible as his sister, as he refused all forms of a rubber or latex nipple. A friend of mine declared once that her baby would not take a pacifier, which I had found hard to believe. Sure, all babies loved pacifiers! You just had to hold it gently in place until they got used to it. Katie would go to sleep with one in her mouth and one in each chubby fist. However, Andrew would have none of it. My husband declared once, after a frustrating evening when I went shopping, that Andrew would rather inhale milk than drink it from a bottle.

Indeed, he was a stubborn little man over how he drank his milk, and by the time he was two months old we gave up even trying to supplement him. All stress was off, and for the next eight months we snuggled and he grew long and lean. What a little cuddler he was! I was constantly amazed at how he could mould his body into mine whether he was feeding or sleeping. I had snuggled many babies who were soft and yielding, but Andrew had an innate ability to fit himself perfectly into the curves of my body and he loved to be held.

And he loved to rock! First it was his baby swing and, as he got bigger, he started rocking in his high chair. It got to the point where he was rocking and bouncing all around the kitchen, so much so that eating became a distant need. So we had to get another chair, the old-fashioned kind that wouldn't move. And he loved to spin things. He could find things to spin that I never knew spun. Fans fascinated him. I remember taking him shopping, and he would throw his arms wide and get such pleasure out of looking up at the spinning fans overheard in the grocery store. When he started crawling there were two places that were his favourites: he would either sit opening and closing the cupboard doors, or plant himself in front of Katie's bookshelf and gently turn the pages of books. He could be engrossed in either activity for hours.

I took all of this in stride and never thought much of these little things. One of the first times a bell went off in my head was when he took his first steps at one year old. He started walking on his tippytoes. Hadn't I read somewhere that this could be a sign of a neurological problem? I tried to massage his ankles and show him how to put his feet flat to the floor, and in a few weeks he started putting his full foot on the floor and began walking.

During this time we also introduced cow's milk into his diet, as he had finally gotten over the hurdle of drinking from a bottle. That happened at around ten months, and when he made the switch, he did it completely. Oh, how he loved his bottle! He would sit in his play centre and throw his head back, and his eyes would roll up into his head with pure pleasure. However, it quickly became obvious that the more milk he drank, the more it didn't agree with him. For one thing, milk made him constipated. His bowel movements were hard, almost like chalk, and he would cry and have so much difficulty. The solution was to water down his milk. First he got half-and-half, and then I started putting only a few ounces of milk in and topping it up with water. That, plus a daily diet of prunes, helped us manage.

The summer he was eighteen months old, he loved to venture outdoors. His favourite activities were running from car to car, reading licence plates from parked vehicles in the cul-de-sac, and throwing countless rocks down the grate. He loved anything involving water, and swimming was a favourite pastime, although baths were nothing but a huge mess. He loved to splash, and regardless of what we said, he would drown the bathroom floor with water. Also, at this age he took to jumping and bouncing on the couch. He would spend hours and hours going up and down and talking toddler gibberish to himself.

That fall we hired a babysitter to come in during the days when my husband and I were both at work. I remember coming home one afternoon and she had written on the chalkboard all the words

Andrew could say. The board was completely full of words like "butterfly," "dog," "horse," "cat," "Mom," "Dad," and "Katie" (which he pronounced *Tse-tse*). We would sit with photos and, while I pointed, he would name each person and would always refer to himself as "Andooo."

Things changed dramatically that January when he turned two. First he developed a nasty ear infection. Three rounds of antibiotics did not clear it up. I would come home and he would be rocking non-stop in the chair. When I would get him out to play on the floor with me, he would scream and climb back up in the chair and continue to rock. My husband said not to worry; he was in pain and his eardrums were close to bursting. But then other things started to happen.

One of the biggest shocks was when he stopped looking at me. During change time on his diaper table, we would always play games, with me blowing on his belly and both of us laughing. But he would no longer meet my eyes, regardless of what I tried. And then he started losing his words. When I pointed to pictures, he would still name Tse-tse, Mugga, Poppy, Mom, and Dad, but when I pointed at a picture of him, he would scream and refuse to say his name.

I told our family doctor and, around Easter, she made a referral to Child Development at the Janeway Children's Hospital. So I waited. The ear infection seemed to clear up, but the words did not come back, the rocking and bouncing continued, as did the constant opening and closing of doors. June came, and still I had not heard from Child Development and I was starting to panic. I called and was told it took three months to get an appointment. It was going into the fourth month, so she gave me an appointment over the phone for April 27. I was shocked. Ten months! My child needed help now. I knew something was wrong, and we could not wait ten whole months.

My husband calmed me. He was convinced everything was going to be okay. He reasoned that Andrew would have me home with him for the summer and we would enrol in daycare in September and catch up to all the developmental milestones.

So I got busy with other things, such as getting an appointment with a speech language pathologist to find out what was going on with his loss of words. I also made appointments to get his hearing checked, as it was evident there were issues. Andrew could not, or would not, listen. In the house, I would call out, "Andrew? Where are you? Andrew?" and he would never respond or come to my calls. Most times I would find him sitting in front of the bookshelf or playing with his letter puzzles. He also did not mind the tone of my voice. Whether I spoke to him sternly or gently, it did not seem to make a difference. All I had to do was breathe the word "no" and sensitive Katie would burst into tears, but not Andrew. I could scream at him, red-faced and angry, and he would completely ignore me. I would turn the TV volume up on bust and then press the mute button. He would barely blink. However, all hearing tests came back normal.

At the first speech language appointment, my husband and I went in and talked for nearly two hours about Andrew's history. In the office there was a play farm with animals and little doors that opened and closed. Andrew loved little houses, and all the time we talked he was completely absorbed in playing with the farm. As our appointment drew to a close, the speech pathologist pointed out that he thought there were other things going on with Andrew. For one thing, he said, most children were not able to sit and focus so intently on something for close to two hours without even looking up. To us, that was Andrew. He had intense powers of concentration when he was interested in something. We were soon to learn the word "perseverate."

April 27 slowly rolled around, and the night before the appointment, my husband and I talked about how the next day we expected Andrew would be diagnosed with autism. However, both of us agreed that we thought it was "mild." He was three years and three months old.

The next day, after a twenty-minute appointment, the pediatrician diagnosed Andrew with full-blown autism. When we asked what she meant by "full-blown," she said they did not use the terms "mild" or "severe" but used an analogy, comparing autism to the common cold. She said Andrew had the "flu-like variety." We asked what we could expect. She said she thought Andrew would be verbal and, by the time he was ten, he would probably only want to talk about things he was interested in, such as trains.

I remember tears running down my cheeks while looking over at my husband and watching his face turn red. Andrew sat at a small table and played with yet another farm toy. He picked up a book, but instead of opening it, he held it close to the side of his eye and moved the book around so he could study the edge. He was oblivious to what was happening. The pediatrician gave me a huge folder of resources and said that a formal diagnosis would be made using the Childhood Autism Rating Scale (CARS) and that five individuals from multiple disciplines would do the rating independently. She scheduled that appointment for the following week.

By the time we got out into our truck, my world had gone grey. I had thought I was ready for Andrew to be diagnosed with autism, but hearing it was completely different. I was angry, I was in shock, and I was upset beyond all belief. I looked back at my little boy in his car seat and passed him a cheesie, which he munched on happily. In my mind, my son was gone. Instead, I had a different child, one I did not know.

When we got home, I opened the folder to the first page, which was the poem "Welcome to Holland." Holland! I didn't want to go to Holland and I didn't care how beautiful the tulips were. I slammed the folder shut, stuffed it deep in the cupboard, and never opened it again.

That long afternoon I sat in our kitchen and tried to get a grip on my grief. I will never forget my husband standing on our patio and assuring me that nothing had changed. Andrew was the same little boy he was that morning, we were good parents, and we were going to be awesome parents now. The sun came out a little around him as he said this, and I was determined he was right.

So, what to do? Well, it was time to get busy doing everything possible.

The next day I started to make phone calls. First I called the Autism Society, Newfoundland and Labrador, which was a fountain of information. They explained to me that we were actually very fortunate to have gotten a diagnosis of autism, as it opened the doors to many resources. *Fortunate to get a diagnosis?* I was at a loss. However, it was explained to me that many parents knew something was wrong, but for whatever reason their child was not diagnosed and thus they were not able to avail of resources.

And the big resource was ABA home therapy provided by the government. Okay, what was ABA? Applied behaviour analysis, and we would be able to start in September with a therapist for thirty hours a week in our home. In addition, I could enrol him in a therapeutic daycare.

When I think back, I wonder why I did not take time off work. All year I had been preparing to move into administration, and when the job offer came, I hesitated. I was working with a great new principal, who kindly explained that my schedule would actually be more flexible to go to appointments. As well, my new role required me to work closely with parents and students in special education and to delve deeper into learning about behaviour. Everything I learned at work was almost directly applicable to what was going on at home, and vice versa.

We had to wait all summer to start these programs, so I spent the evenings reading late into the night. I learned about the gluten-free casein-free (GFCF) diet. No one had mentioned this to me. However, when I read about how the digestive systems of people with autism only partially broke down the proteins casein and gluten to produce a type of opiate, it all started to come together. I knew milk did not agree with Andrew, so the first step was to take him off milk. By this time he was only getting small amounts during the day, so I switched completely to watered-down, low-acid apple juice. He was mostly a protein eater, so cutting down on bread and gluten was not a big deal.

That first summer of his diagnosis, we took a family trip to PEI. We dragged our pop-up trailer behind us and made the trek across the island and then took the ferry to a campsite where we enjoyed the Anne of Green Gables site and countless water parks. Oh, how Andrew loved the water! He would get so excited he would rub his hands together under his chin until I thought the skin would peel away.

Like most families who have children with autism, we had heard that the divorce rate is exceptionally high: at around 80%. My husband and I were determined that we would not be part of that statistic. However, times were busy and many evenings the needs of those around us, rather than each other, became the priority. But not every evening. Friday evenings were ours. We let the kids basically do whatever they wanted while we would sit in the kitchen together and talk and laugh and dance. We would order takeout pizza and spread a blanket on the floor and have "pizza picnics" with the kids. Later, I learned that the statistic of 80% was an urban legend, but I would not trade those Friday evenings for anything.

That fall we interviewed and hired a psychology graduate to start Andrew's ABA therapy and enrolled him in Daybreak Daycare. I went with him a few times and it was absolutely terrible. It was awful to watch the therapy and his "table work" at home, where he would scream and hit to try to get away. And at first the hitting worked and he would be told to go to his room. The behaviour management specialist who came once a week explained that by hitting, he was getting exactly what he wanted: to get out of his table work and go to his room, where he could read and do what he wanted. So the therapist was instructed that if he hit, he still had to sit there and be told to keep his hands to himself. The hitting decreased. It was hard to watch my son misbehave and hit someone and have to say and do nothing. And he could scream—ear-splitting screams, which caused his therapist to take several days off due to the ringing in her ears.

By Christmas our first ABA therapist had quit. My husband and I agreed that we needed to find the best person possible, and we were willing to go into debt to do that. Instead of offering the government rate of $9.25 an hour, we decided to top it up to $14.25 an hour, and instead of thirty hours we hired someone for forty hours a week. That was a difference of $300 a week. We recognized that it was of upmost importance that the therapist be child-oriented, and we were most likely to find this quality in someone who had a primary education degree. And we found her! She was marvellous with him and, under her tutelage, our son started to make leaps and bounds in development. That September she was offered a full-time job teaching, so off we went again and found another primary teacher. For three years in a row we were fortunate to find amazing teachers to work with our son. And work they did.

Compliance was a huge issue with Andrew. He could do so many things, but only when he wanted to and not on anyone else's schedule. Telling him to pick up his toys because it was time for bed, or that he had to put his shoes and coat on, could lead to meltdowns. He would get warnings that if he didn't comply he would face some sort of punishment. The threat of punishment had no effect. The sterner we got, the angrier he would become. I would tell him that it was enough and he would need a time out. By the time it reached this level, he was beyond listening and would kick and scream on the floor. Trying to pick him up was like trying to get hold of a piece of spaghetti, and he would kick and hit the whole way to time out. All the regular discipline routines would not and did not work with him.

After some research, I came across a book called *The Explosive Child* by Ross Greene. It said we could have a disciplined child, but the method of discipline had to change. I read about the "basket" method and then taught it to my family. Everyone understood how Andrew would enter "vapour lock" only to be fuelled by threats of consequence. We, the adults, were in control, and with a little foresight and communication, we could avoid most episodes of meltdown. Our lives changed, and although we didn't completely eliminate the meltdowns, we were at least not experiencing them on a daily basis.

Between episodes of meltdowns, Andrew was actually a very happy and agreeable toddler. We used his echolalia—repetition of another person's words—to our advantage, as it was easy to get him to repeat back to you word for word anything you said. To anyone listening, it would seem like we had complete compliance.

Andrew learned to talk, but not in a way that I had ever heard of before. For one thing, he heard things differently than we did. He could mimic almost any sound in the environment, and you could tell he didn't distinguish these other sounds from speech. To him it was all a form of communication. One afternoon, while lying down on his grandmother's bed for a nap, the heater cut in, making a strange clicking noise. He looked at me and repeated it exactly, as if it were something very important he had to say.

One fall evening, when he was three and a half, he was sitting in the bathtub, happily splashing into oblivion, when he said, "S-T-E-P-H-A-N-I-E spells Stephanie!" Huh? I tried to get him to repeat it, but he did things on his own time and not when someone asked. Shortly after, I was working on the computer and Andrew came over, stood next to me, and read a word on the screen. I pulled up a new page and started typing one word after the other. Stephanie, Mom, Dad, Mugga, Katie, then all the colours, animals, food, familiar objects around the house, and he read them off, one by one. Here was my son, at three and a half years old, who could not put a sentence together on his own, reading words I had typed on a screen. Four pages later, I was nearing the end of an exhaustive list when I typed the word "gross." He hauled back his head, spit on the keyboard, then proudly proclaimed, "GROSS!" I knew he was good with letters and could recognize simple words, but I did not quite get the full scope of his ability until that evening.

So, Andrew started reading before he could talk. At his next appointment with the developmental pediatrician, she said he had "hyperlexia," the precocious ability to read words without prior training. So it was on to more reading late into the night. I found out that between five and ten per cent of children with autism also had hyperlexia. Some thought it should be a separate disorder, but all reports said that we were very fortunate indeed, as this "splinter ability" could help tremendously in communication.

We started writing lists of everything. 1. Eat breakfast. 2. Get dressed. 3. Brush your teeth. 4. Put on your coat and shoes. 5. Get in the car. Some sources told us that even though children with hyperlexia could read, their comprehension lagged behind . . . however, that did not seem to be the case with Andrew. Later, when he was tested, we saw that his reading was in the ninety-ninth percentile and his word comprehension was only slightly lower, in the ninety-eighth percentile.

We made lists upon lists, and for concepts that were more complicated we did social stories. They ranged from such topics as "Andrew is nice to people" and "How to make friends" to "Andrew gets his hair cut." Actually, social stories and exposure therapy helped tremendously with haircuts. He hated haircuts. It would take three people to hold him down amidst tears, snot, hair, and perspiration. One time, my husband took him and decided to sit and hold him in his lap, but Andrew nixed that plan by peeing on him.

The social stories started off simply. I would use PowerPoint and search for graphics online and incorporate images from my own wide selection of photos. As well, I would add in SpongeBob SquarePants or other characters I thought he would be more apt to take directions from. I continued to produce these for him. He improved so much with it that, over time, it was only the really big things that needed social stories.

When Andrew was eight years old we bought a new house and moved neighbourhoods. That first day we drove home, and when he saw the For Sale sign on the lawn of our old house, he was so upset he collapsed in the car. Social story #29 came into effect. By the time we moved, he was the most adjusted and accepting of the entire family. The following September he also transferred schools, and for grade four he started attending a new school that was very active and socially conscious about autism.

For several years we had wondered how to tell Andrew he had autism. I had read many suggestions, but the time had not presented itself. His new school was holding Autism Awareness Month and there were a dozen or more students in the school with a diagnosis of autism. One October night, as I was tucking him in, he said to me quite simply, "Mom, do I have autism?" I remember my whole world grinding to a halt. He had figured it out all on his own. I looked at him levelly. "Yes, you were diagnosed with autism when you were three years old." Calmly and gently and with lots of deep-pressure hugging, I tried to explain to him the complex world of autism. He was nine and it was a lot to take in.

For him, autism was the other students he saw around him in his "pull out" classes. He knew they were all different, and to be grouped under the same label was something he struggled with. He was at first angry, and the blow to his self-esteem took a toll. In his frustration, he told me several times that he hated himself and he just wanted to run out into traffic. I put in a call to psychiatry, but by the time the slow wheels of that spun about, things had finally settled down. The last incident was during a drive home from his grandmother's house, when he threatened to jump out of the car. I pulled over to the side of the road and we had a long talk.

Speaking of his grandmother, I would attribute a large amount of his development and success to her commitment and work with him. Shortly after Andrew's diagnosis, my father passed away, and she made it a major goal in her life to work with Andrew and do whatever she could to help him. It was not the work of advocacy or attending events; it was a more personal and hands-on approach that she took. His ABA therapy stopped after kindergarten, but she picked up where it left off. Every day she would pick him up from school and they would spend several hours together until we got home.

Andrew's grandmother valued the importance of routine. First she would feed him yogourt and chocolate and lots of water. Then they would hit the books. On occasion, my husband and I got to witness the uphill battle of what homework hour with Mugga exactly entailed. It wasn't easy for either of them. There was the year that he would hide his math book, and other stressful evenings with him cracking pencils and screaming on the floor. But he had met his match with his grandmother. She was no shirker of duties and, over the years, she instilled in him the value of getting his work completed to the best of his ability. Most importantly, they talked. She was interested in his day and everything that was going on with him. The bond they have formed is amazing, and to this day the role she plays in his life is profound.

We emphasized to Andrew that autism gave him several special gifts. One of these was his ability to perseverate on his topic of interest. When he was engaged he would eat, breathe, and sleep the topic until he gained a mastery that far surpassed what a typical person could perform.

The pediatrician was right all those years ago in that he loved to talk about his topic of interest. His eyes would light up, and he loved to explain things to people. However, she was not right in that his interests were limited. Fortunately, the topics changed over the years. There was the time he took an intense interest in everything about space and could rhyme off a million facts about the planets and the solar system. Then he moved on to anatomy and studied the physical systems and parts of the body. He also took an intense interest in two particular video games—*SpongeBob SquarePants: Battle for Bikini Bottom* and *Punch-Out!!* for the Wii. When Andrew turned ten, he published online a sixty-page manual or walk-through of the SpongeBob SquarePants game.

While growing up, Andrew always had an interest in graveyards. As a special treat I would take him to these peaceful places and he would move from grave to grave, entranced by the information on the headstones. He would read the names and dates of birth and death. This developed into an interest in genealogy, and when he was eleven he started working on our family tree. I remember him telling me he had reached 1,000 names on our tree. Then it was on to 2,000, 3,000, and, three years later, he now has close to 8,000 names. He can trace our family back to a Viking ancestor in 780 AD. Although he has it online, it is also in his head, and he can go back about forty generations just on pure memory.

Many people with autism also have to deal with anxiety. Andrew has been fortunate that anxiety has not taken over his life. However, a few things make him anxious. He becomes stressed when he has to make a decision, even something as simple as what type of treat he would like to have. He calls it "decision fever." There was also a time he was very anxious about teenagers. When his sister turned thirteen, he worried that she would turn into a mindless, stereotypical teen. I think one of the happiest days of her life was when he finally turned thirteen, too, and he realized that not all teenagers are created alike.

Andrew is not too concerned about social situations. He has a few friends in school, but other than that, he doesn't want to hang out with friends around the neighbourhood. Most days he takes the dog for a walk, bounces on his trampoline, and goes out and about with family on adventures and errands. His best friend is his first cousin Brianna, who lives in Gander. They visit each other often, and when they are together it is a joy to hear their laughter ring through the house.

Another great thing he has been doing is keeping a journal. He started it when he was six and, although he sometimes finds his handwriting hard to decipher, he loves to go back through all the things he has written. Last year in English class, he had to write about one of his proudest accomplishments, and he wrote how he decided in grade six that he did not need a student assistant at school any more. He loves school, and after his first day of grade seven, one of his teachers called to say what a pleasure it was to see him smiling from ear to ear with genuine happiness to be back. Last year he made the honour roll and proudly came home with an award pin. We were so proud and so very hopeful.

Andrew talks about wanting to go to university. He says that one day he would like to be married and have children. A few years ago, I was asked during an interview what I wished for him in life and I said, "For him to be happy." Most days he is indeed that.

Several years ago I once again came across the poem "Welcome to Holland." This time I was ready to read and appreciate the message. But in the end I realize I am not in Holland, and neither is any parent of any child that I know. Nothing about parenting is anything anyone expects. Even though we have all embarked on different journeys, we all chose the same thing. We chose to be parents.

After twenty-three years working as an educator, today Bridget Ricketts is the principal of the new Waterford Valley High School in St. John's. She is married to Douglas Ballam and they live in Mount Pearl with their two children, Katie and Andrew, and their pets, Coco and Pepper.

A Window into Autism through DNA

by Stephen W. Scherer

Professor Stephen Scherer, Ph.D., D.Sc., FRSC is a scientist at the Hospital for Sick Children and the University of Toronto. Over the years, his research group has made numerous contributions to medical genetics, including mapping, sequencing, and disease gene studies of the human genome. He also contributed to discoveries of global gene copy number variation (CNV), revealing CNV to be the most abundant type of variation of human DNA. His group also found CNV to contribute to the cause of autism.

Ten years ago, autism was an enigma, a black box, with very little known about it. In my opinion, the most important achievement of the past decade has been generating awareness of what autism is and, equally important, what it is not. A large part of that awareness came from new information stemming from scientific research. Our group and others have shown that autism, previously considered to be strictly a behavioural disorder, can have a biological basis—and that genes are often involved. In fact, dozens of different genes have now been identified to be susceptibility factors involved in autism, but this is just the tip of the iceberg.

Even though still in progress, these genetic discoveries are groundbreaking, since doctors can begin to use the information to facilitate more accurate clinical diagnosis and sometimes even enable earlier identification, which is critical for optimal outcomes. We have also now identified many new molecules that are involved in autism, and these serve as targets that might be modulated by new medicines that are now being developed. The future for autism research is exciting.

Below, I have assembled written answers to the questions I am asked most often at seminars I give. Wherever possible, I have emphasized information arising from evidence-based research and seeded in some commentary.

What is autism?

Autism is short for autism spectrum disorder (ASD), a group of neurodevelopmental conditions characterized by core deficits in three domains of function—namely, communication, repetitive or stereotypic behaviours, and social interaction. The degree of impairment among individuals with ASD is variable, but the impact on families is universally life-altering. Core ASD symptoms can also be accompanied by anxiety, sleep problems, seizures, and gastrointestinal or other medical problems. It is important to stress that autism is not a single disorder, but really a collection of disorders that have common clinical symptoms. Even identical twins (who share identical DNA) can vary in their symptoms.

I've heard one parent describe their child—who's on the severe end of the spectrum—as being "stuck in the terrible twos 24/7 magnified by 1,000." On the mild end is Asperger's syndrome.

Individuals afflicted with Asperger's may only have deficits in their social interaction skills. Some people believe Albert Einstein had Asperger's. The movie *Rain Man* presented the autistic savant type of autism, where individuals exhibit some form of brilliance in contrast to their overall limitations. Less than 1% of individuals with ASD fall in this group.

All these different forms of ASD—ranging from "severe" to "high-functioning" and everything in between, tend to be grouped together, often leading to misunderstanding or misinterpretation of autism and how it affects the individuals and their families. Communication is a vital component in proper autism diagnosis. It is also a vital aspect of how autism is portrayed to families, policy-makers, and the public.

In a recent presentation I delivered at the United Nations, I defined autism in the following way: "The impairments in social interaction, in communication, and in play . . . that represent the core features involved in autism can strike at the very heart of what it means to be an individual, perhaps even stealing their free will." In mentioning free will, I thought it would capture the attention of the delegate from the United Nations, which it did, along with stimulating many interesting discussions.

How can you tell if a child has autism? Specifically, what are the warning signs and how do doctors screen for the disorder?

Lee Steel, a mother of an autistic boy, and Professor Wendy Roberts—both of our University of Toronto research team—generated a wonderful document called *Autism Spectrum Disorder: Information for Parents*. It is available for free at:

http://www.tcag.ca/documents/Autism_Spectrum_Disorder_info_for_Parents.pdf

I highly recommend looking at this paper. The warning signs they highlight include:

— problems with social interaction: for example, talking to, working, or playing with others;
— unusual interest in objects: that is, hyper-fixating on certain toys, appliances, or machines;
— need for sameness: a change to a routine may lead to severe tantrums;
— great variation in abilities: for example, the child may not be able to play a simple game with a friend, but will be able to understand and operate a computer;
— not meeting language milestones or not talking at all;
— sensory hypersensitivity: that is, strong reactions to sunlight or loud noises; and
— repeated actions or body movements: for example, spinning, hand flapping, and walking on tippytoes.

Children with autism might also experience difficulties with smell and distinguishing the colour or texture of certain foods or clothes. Parents often comment, before their child's diagnosis, that they thought their child was just very shy. The terms "trapped within oneself" and "sticky personality" are often used.

What causes autism?

There is great debate in the public about what causes autism. The best scientific evidence indicates that genes—one's DNA—are most likely the culprit in one way or another—directly or indirectly—in a majority of individuals with ASD.

Some specific ASD-causing genes have now been identified and are now used in diagnostic testing. Combined, these genes account for approximately 20% of individuals with autism. Some of these genes include *SHANK2*, *SHANK3*, *SCN2A*, *NLGN3*, *NLGN4*, *NRXN1*, *PTCHD1*, which make proteins that control how brain cells communicate with each other.

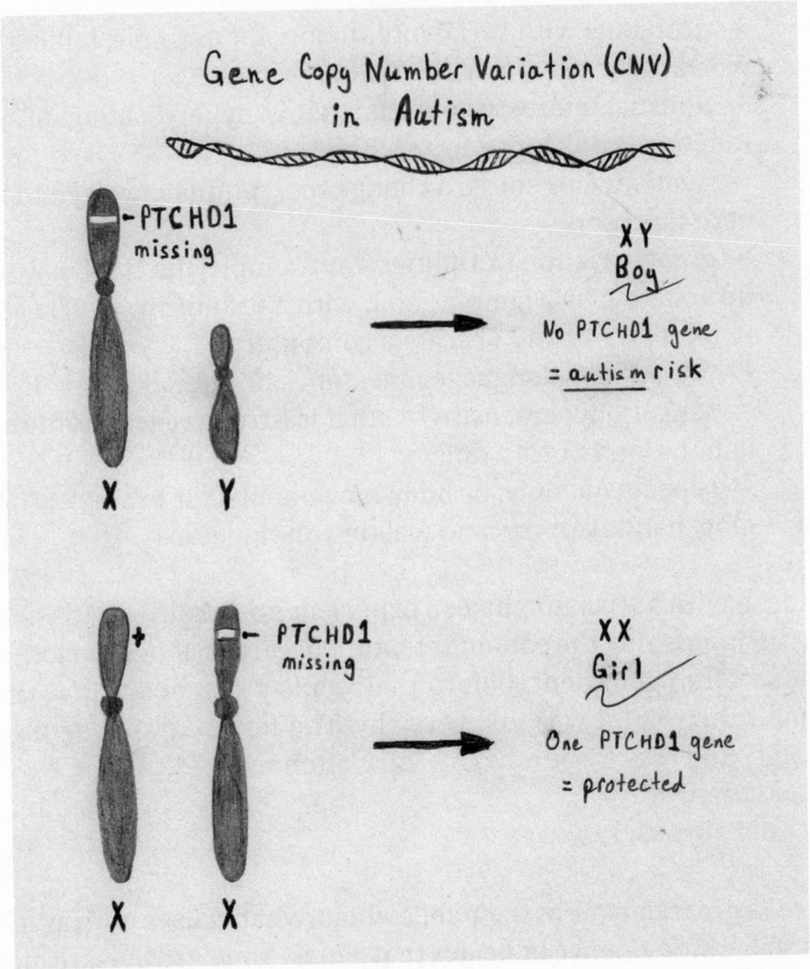

A hand-drawn illustration showing the concept of gene copy number variation (CNV) and its role in autism. Dr. Stephen Scherer was nominated for the Nobel Prize for this breakthrough in autism markers. Photo courtesy of Stephen W. Scherer.

Our work has shown that copy number variations (CNVs) in these specific genes—that is, one copy or three copies of a specific gene (or set of genes) being present instead of the typical two—can cause ASD. There are genetic tests available for these forms of autism, and the technique called clinical microarrays, which measures gene copy number, has become the "standard of care," facilitating ASD diagnosis and treatment. In my province of Ontario in Canada, approximately 1,000 microarray tests are run each year for ASD and related disorders.

With the astounding breakthroughs that are now starting to enable complete genome sequencing, which decodes all 3 billion genetic letters in the DNA blueprint, we expect that we'll soon find even more ASD risk genes (that are missed by older technologies like microarrays). I anticipate there are several hundred genes involved in ASD, and with enough investment we'll find all of them in the next five years.

In fact, I have the distinct privilege of leading the monumental international MSSNG (finding the *missing* information in autism) project: a collaboration between Autism Speaks and Google and my research team. Together, we are creating—and sharing through open science—the world's largest genomic database for autism research. Our objective is to sequence the genomes of 10,000 families with autism in order to find all of the genetic factors involved. MSSNG's goal is to provide the best resource for researchers around the world to enable the identification of many subtypes of autism, which will lead to better diagnostics and new medicines. We believe individualized medicine will come into its own for autism, as we recognize the individual constellations of risk factors, varied prognoses, and potential treatment opportunities to be applied differentially to each person affected.

We are also involving the families that donate their DNA for the research so that they can start to get the answers to questions they so desperately need addressed. MSSNG is our "moon shot" for autism research, and we welcome partnership with anyone who shares our vision.

It is important to note that birth complications and drugs like valproic acid and thalidomide seem to cause autism in a rare few—less than 1%. Therefore, non-genetic environmental factors are also involved, but we don't yet really know to what extent. It will be important to further study how the environment causes ASD, as well as how the environment influences genetic risk factors.

Another major research advance has been that animal models carrying mutations in the same genes that cause autism in humans can sometimes have their autistic features reversed when treated with specific therapeutics that target the dysregulated genetic pathways involved. The identification of all of these new diagnostic and therapeutic pathways has depended upon the earlier genetic discoveries.

How common is autism?

Statistics from the Centre for Disease Control indicate ASD affects one in 120 children and a startling one in approximately every seventy boys. There is much in the media about autism being on the rise. It is important to clarify that while the number of new diagnoses of autism cases is indeed increasing each year, this could represent several things including (1) a true increase in the incidence of autism, (2) more public and medical awareness leading to more ASD diagnoses, (3) "shifting" diagnoses—that is, diagnoses previously carrying another label may be rediagnosed as ASD, and (4) all or a combination of the previously mentioned factors.

What is for sure is that ASD is not going away, and while most of the existing prevalence data comes from studies conducted in North America and Europe, statistics originating from other populations (recently Korea, Japan, Mexico) seem to reveal similar numbers indicating autism has no boundaries.

Why does autism affect more boys than girls?

To be honest, we really don't fully know. Most studies show a 4:1 gender bias in autism, in particular when you consider the more severe forms of autism. There are many thoughts on why this is. One of the more interesting ideas suggests that through evolution males developed genes that impacted focus and survival in isolation, making it easier for them to "hunt and gather" during long trips where they were isolated. Females, on the other hand, were more involved in taking care of families. Their evolution favoured different types of genes. Therefore, in today's society a typical male is much closer to being "autistic," and a slight genetic or environmental disturbance may push them across an autism threshold more easily than is the case for females.

Another explanation is that some of the genes involved in ASD are on the X-chromosome. Boys are boys because they inherit one X-chromosome from their mother and one Y-chromosome from their father. If a boy's X-chromosome is missing a specific gene such as the X-linked *PTCHD1* gene our team discovered, they will be at high risk of developing ASD. Girls are different in that, even if they are missing one *PTCHD1* gene, by nature they always carry a second X-chromosome, shielding them from ASD. While females are protected, autism could appear in future generations in these families, especially in boys. The *PTCHD1* story is very compelling, but this autism gene still only accounts for about 1% of all families. In the end, I suspect there are several contributing factors. If anything is simple in autism, it's that in autism everything is complex.

Do you believe autism can be cured?

There are new studies that show that every child who undergoes intensive behavioural intervention therapy improves in some way, and this is now being translated into real-world impact through broad training initiatives and in a growing number of jurisdictions. In fact, I have heard rare stories of some children having full or near-full recoveries. The most important factor leading to positive outcomes, however, is to start such interventions early and, in the best-case scenario, even before the first signs of autism appear.

This is where our genetic discoveries will have a great impact because they can facilitate early diagnosis. For example, with a simple blood or saliva sample we can assess the genome and, in an increasing number of instances, find a genetic marker that indicates the individual (baby or even fetus) is at high risk of having autism or some type of neurodevelopmental disorder. These tests are really now only making their way from research labs into hospital diagnostic labs.

Unfortunately, there are not yet any effective drugs that treat autism. However, with our many new gene discoveries, pharmaceutical targets are increasingly being found and companies are developing drugs for them. The progress looks very encouraging.

The future

My dream is that one day there will be a pill developed that can help alleviate at least a few of the core deficits in autism in some individuals, and maybe all of the deficits in others. Individuals with ASD might have their own unique genetic form of autism, so this might complicate coming up with a "magic bullet." We are, however, finding that autism risk genes all seem to work together in the same biochemical pathways, so there may be common targets universal drugs can make an impression on.

Either way, I don't intend to retire until there are more effective treatments for autism. If humans can put a man on the moon and learn how to sequence our own genomes, we can surely figure autism out. We have already opened a window into autism through genetic research, but there is so much further to go. I suspect, through the process of researching autism, we may stumble upon an understanding of something even more profound than new treatments, that is, the essence of what it means to be human.

Stephen W. Scherer has won numerous awards and was selected as a Thomson Reuters Citation Laureate for his contribution to the field of physiology and medicine "for the discovery of large-scale copy number variation and its association with specific dis-

eases." These Citation Laureates have become commonly known as Thomson Reuters "picks" for the Nobel Prize. Dr. Scherer also leads the Autism Speaks–Google MSSNG Program, which aims to sequence the genomes of 10,000 families with autism.

Publisher's Note and Acknowledgements

My experience with autism begins with my son. By the time he was two years old, my family and I observed that something was almost certainly hindering his development. He had been late crawling, walking, potty training, and he hadn't started speaking yet. His only means of communicating his needs were pointing and screaming. He wouldn't respond or acknowledge when we called him by name.

The first two doctors we consulted assured us that my son was fine and that he would grow and develop at his own rate. Not satisfied with that, my father insisted we bring my son back to our family physician, Dr. Karl Misik, who then referred us to a team of specialists. On September 27, 2000, the day before his third birthday, my son was diagnosed with mild to moderate autism, leaning, the specialists said, toward the moderate end.

The diagnosis presented a challenge made more daunting by the wait-list for those applying for ABA therapy. Applied behavioural analysis is a program of intensive one-on-one therapy in which a therapist visits the home thirty hours a week and works to bring out the child's hidden gifts. This was and still is the best possible early intervention for children who are on the autism spectrum. However, my son was number eleven on the wait-list, which, we calculated, meant he could be waiting two years to begin the program.

Luck and politics were on our side. In 2001, Roger Grimes, then premier of Newfoundland and Labrador, announced a provincial budget with a sizable contribution going toward early childhood development. My son and the ten children ahead of him were approved for ABA therapy right away.

My family's luck prevailed further when we hired a remarkable therapist, Angela Boutcher, a dedicated and attentive worker who has a genuine love for children. She visited our home and used a variety of tools at her disposal, including what I learned was called "communicative temptation." This is a technique whose purpose is to gently interrupt repetitive behaviours and *tempt* the child to speak out.

It worked.

By October 2001, at four years of age, my son had gone from non-verbal to speaking in complete sentences and showing astonishing levels of concentration, memory, observation, and empathy. Applied behavioural analysis therapy had bridged for us what had been a chasm. Suddenly, a world of possibilities was open for him—school, communication, learning, and even employment—where before there were none.

More therapy followed: speech therapy, occupational therapy, and craniosacral massage. My son thrived. After watching a half-hour Claymation children's show called *Dragon*, he would recite the entire episode by memory. When we got in our car, he would follow with his finger our route on his map of St. John's. He craved information, and we supplied it for him: books on volcanoes, weather, ancient cities, animals, geography, world history. Whenever family members travelled outside the province, we brought him maps of the places we had visited.

There were some issues, or what my son's lead specialist, Dr. Victoria Crosbie, might call "aberrant behaviours." The sound of the toilet flushing frightened him and delayed his potty training. Rain, wind, and thunder caused him a great deal of anxiety. One day while grocery shopping, we brought him to a supermarket on Stavanger Drive, in the east end of St. John's. He screamed upon entering through the front door, though what was causing him distress—the smells, the sounds, or the lighting inside the store—we couldn't say. Visiting other stores was a source of fun and pleasure for him; he would walk up and down aisles, peering sideways at the colours and shapes of products on the shelves as he passed them, not stopping until it was time to go home.

These issues persisted to some degree over the years—I remember my son's grade six teacher telling me that my son, whose desk faced the classroom's large window, would become agitated if it was raining, snowing, or windy outside—but over time his anxiety subsided to manageable levels. Socialization remained a challenge. He tended not to initiate conversation and engage with his peers or his teachers. However, he would always respond cheerfully.

My son with Canadian acting legend Gordon Pinsent in 2009.

Interestingly, throughout his elementary, junior high, and high school years, my son remained a straight-A student. His grades were high enough in grade nine that he was accepted into the International Baccalaureate (IB) program at Holy Heart High School. He graduated from grades ten and eleven with ninety-percentile averages.

Today, he is attending grade twelve, his last year of high school. He is bright, well-adjusted, and still craves information. He has expressed great interest in business, economics, and world travel. One of the highlights of his year is our family's annual vacation to Las Vegas. He wants to visit Dubai one day, and to go on a Mediterranean cruise.

Recently, while on our way to Costco on Stavanger Drive, he turned to me and asked, "Do you remember the supermarket that used to be next to Costco? Didn't you find that place scary? I did."

Roseanne Hickey-Hatchett's story on sensory processing disorder immediately came to mind.

In the fall of 2013, I read a book called *The Spark: A Mother's Journey of Nurturing Genius* by Kristine Barnett. Her son, Jacob Barnett, is autistic and, as the name of the book suggests, a genius. He attended university classes in astrophysics at age nine, he expanded on Albert Einstein's Theory of Relativity at age twelve, and today as a teenager he is one of the world's most promising physicists. Getting there wasn't easy, though. Jacob's parents were vigilant and got him the help he needed at the right time to bring out his extraordinary gifts.

I couldn't help but draw parallels between Jacob Barnett and my son. They have both overcome great odds to become capable, intelligent young men for whom the world is their oyster. And so the idea for publishing a book similar to Kristine Barnett's excellent work took root.

My parents, Garry and Margo Cranford, and I own and operate Flanker Press, the largest trade book publishing company in Newfoundland and Labrador. Since 1994 we have published approximately 300 titles. More than thirty have won or have been nominated for provincial, national, and international literary awards, and since 2009, ten of them have appeared on the *Globe and Mail*'s bestsellers list. However, *Autism: The Gift That Needs to Be Opened* is the first of our published books that has a deeply personal meaning for us.

My son with Holocaust survivor Philip Riteman and his wife, Dorothy (Smilestein) Riteman in St. John's, November 2013. Flanker Press published Mr. Riteman's memoir, *Millions of Souls*, in 2010.

Autism: the gift that needs to be opened. I can't take credit for the title of this book. It's my father's brainchild. Taking the idea that autism is a gift one step further, it's important to note the passive voice in the title, because *autism is a gift that can't open itself.*

Today, I think about the first two doctors who misdiagnosed my son. I think about the wait-lists for assessment and applied behavioural analysis therapy, and the reality that, as a result, many children with autism spectrum disorder will continue to go undiagnosed and untreated. I also think about early intervention and the very short window of opportunity in which treatment will be effective. I reflect on Dr. Stephen Scherer's statement in the story you just read, that "studies . . . show that every child who undergoes intensive behavioural intervention therapy improves in some way."

That's a powerful message for a world that is, by and large, neglecting the needs of children who are on the autism spectrum.

My hope is that parents, educators, doctors, politicians, policy-makers, and advocates will take note of this: one in sixty-eight children is born every day who, with the odds stacked against him or her, will likely fall through the cracks of society. Endless visits by home care workers. Exclusion from school. Institutionalization. The absence of quality of life.

I hope you enjoyed reading these stories. Some, as you know, are stories of success, while others show continued adversity and an uncertain future. We as parents have a responsibility to look after our children in the best way we can, using the best available resources. The playing field may be a little different, but the rules remain the same.

My son with the lovely Elaine Dobbin at the Autism Society, Newfoundland and Labrador's Spring Gala in April 2015.

We have the tools necessary to improve the lives of those who are on the autism spectrum. We just need to find a way to get those tools to them in time.

I have many people to thank for making this book possible. First, I would like to thank the many people who have given generously of their time and creativity to write these stories: Senator Jim Munson, Scott Crocker, Temple Grandin, Katrina Bajzak, Jessica Butt, Krista Preuss-Goodreault, Olivia Goodreault, Dawn Haire-Butt, B. T. Hall, Heather Warner, Laura Hamlyn, Roseanne Hickey-Hatchett, Tom Jackman, Dwayne LaFitte, Sarah MacAulay, Tricia Teeft, Doug McCreary, Michael McCreary, Tori Oliver, Nicole Parsons, Bridget Ricketts, and Stephen W. Scherer. Second, my sincere gratitude to contributors' family and colleagues, who encouraged this book's publication and whose voices have also been added, and are just as important, to the growing chorus of autism awareness and advocacy worldwide: Jeanette Munson, Senator Norman Doyle, Christian Dicks, Cheryl Miller, Sabrina Whyatt, Keliegh Butt, Dr. John K. Crellin, Jim Wellman, Twila LaFitte, Susan McCreary, Jolene Oliver, Gary Collins, Rose Collins, and J. A. Ricketts.

The good people at the Autism Society, Newfoundland and Labrador have been wonderful supporters of this book. I would like to thank: Scott Crocker, Tess Hemeon, Elaine Dobbin, Greg Knott, Kendra Lane, Sarah White, and Suzanne Kenny.

My parents, Garry and Margo Cranford, have been among my son's biggest advocates his whole life. Their guidance and support have been instrumental in bringing out his potential. Thanks, Mom and Dad.

Dr. Victoria Crosbie, Angela Boutcher, Vijay Manocha, Dr. Karl Misik, and Noreen Yetman have played important roles in my son's development over the years. Thank you all.

To the staff at Flanker Press, my heartfelt thanks: Laura Cameron, Jennifer Konieczny, Bob Woodworth, Peter Hanes, Gerard Murphy, Grant Loveys, Randy Drover, and Garry and Margo Cranford.

My thanks as well to graphic designer Graham Blair and editor Robin McGrath, each for doing a marvellous job with this book.

And finally, my biggest thank you goes to my son. This book is for you.

Jerry Cranford
Flanker Press

Suggested Reading

Auer, Christopher and Susan Blumberg and Lucy Jane Miller. *Parenting a Child with Sensory Processing Disorder: A Family Guide to Understanding and Supporting Your Sensory-Sensitive Child*. New Harbinger Publications, 2006.

Ayres, A. Jean. *Sensory Integration and the Child: Understanding Hidden Sensory Challenges*. Western Psychological Services, 2005.

Barnett, Kristine. *The Spark: A Mother's Story of Nurturing Genius*. Random House Canada, 2013.

Bialer, Doreit and Lucy Jane Miller. *No Longer a Secret: Unique Common Sense Strategies for Children with Sensory or Motor Challenges*. Sensory World, 2011.

Biel, Lindsey and Nancy Peske. *Raising a Sensory Smart Child: The Definitive Handbook for Helping Your Child with Sensory Integration Issues*. Penguin Books, 2005.

Centre for Communicable Diseases and Infection Control. *Canadian Guidelines for Sexual Health Education*. Public Health Agency of Canada, 2008.

Collins, Gary and Maggie Rose Parsons. *What Colour is the Ocean?* Flanker Press, 2009.

Cutler, Eustacia. *A Thorn in My Pocket: Temple Grandin's Mother Tells the Family Story*. Future Horizons, 2004.

Grandin, Temple. *Animals in Translation: Using the Mysteries of Autism to Decode Animal Behaviour*. Bloomsbury Publishing, 2005.

Grandin, Temple. *Different . . . Not Less: Inspiring Stories of Achievement and Successful Employment from Adults with Autism, Asperger's, and ADHD*. Future Horizons, 2012.

Grandin, Temple and Margaret M. Scariano. *Emergence: Labeled Autistic*. Grand Central Publishing, 1996.

Granirer, David. *The Happy Neurotic: How Fear and Angst Can Lead to Happiness and Success*. Warwick Publishing, 2006.

Greene, Ross W. *The Explosive Child*. Harper Paperbacks, 2001.

Greenspan, Stanley I. and Serena Wieder. *Engaging Autism: Using the Floortime Approach to Help Children Relate, Communicate, and Think*. Da Capo Press, 2006.

Haddon, Mark. *The Curious Incident of the Dog in the Night-Time*. Anchor Canada, 2004.

Hall, B. T. *Too Many Espresso Beans*. Self-published, 2009.

Hannaford, Carla. *Awakening the Child Heart: Handbook for Global Parenting*. Jamilla Nur Publishing, 2002.

Hannaford, Carla. *Smart Moves: Why Learning is Not All in Your Head*. Great River Books, 2007.

Hill, Mel Reiff and Jay Mays. *The Gender Book*. The Gender Book, 2014.

Hoopmann, Kathy. *All Cats Have Asperger Syndrome*. Jessica Kingsley Publishers, 2006.

Kaufman, Barry Neil. *Son Rise: The Miracle Continues*. H. J. Kramer, 1994.

Kranowitz, Carol Stock. *The Goodenoughs Get in Sync*. Sensory World, 2004.

Kranowitz, Carol Stock. *The Out-of-Sync Child: Recognizing and Coping with Sensory Processing Disorder*. Perigree Books, 2006.

Kranowitz, Carol Stock. *The Out-of-Sync Child Has Fun: Activities for Kids with Sensory Processing Disorder*. Perigree Books, 2006.

LaFitte, Dwayne. *Over by the Harbour*. Flanker Press, 2014.

Lewis, Randy. *No Greatness Without Goodness: How a Father's Love Changed a Company and Sparked a Movement*. Tynedale House Publishers, 2014.

Madaule, Paul. *When Listening Comes Alive: A Guide to Effective Learning and Communication*. Hushion House, 1997.

Miller, Lucy Jane. *Sensational Kids: Hope and Help for Children with Sensory Processing Disorder*. G. P. Putnam's Sons, 2006.

Preuss-Goodreault, Krista and Olivia Goodreault. *May I Be Excused, My Brain is Full: Olivia's Asperger's Story*. Friesen Press, 2012.

Reynolds, John Lawrence. *One Hell of a Ride: How Craig Dobbin Built the World's Largest Helicopter Company*. Douglas & McIntyre, 2009.

Robison, John Elder. *Be Different: My Adventures with Asperger's and My Advice for Fellow Aspergians, Misfits, Families, and Teachers*. Anchor Canada, 2012.

Sex Information and Education Council of Canada. *The Canadian Journal of Human Sexuality*. Sex Information and Education Council of Canada, 2003.

Siegel, Daniel J. and Tina Payne Bryson. *The Whole-Brain Child: 12 Revolutionary Strategies to Nurture Your Child's Developing Mind*. Bantam Books, 2012.

Silberman, Steve. *NeuroTribes: The Legacy of Autism and the Future of Neurodiversity*. Avery, 2015.

Steel, Lee and Wendy Roberts. *Autism Spectrum Disorder: Information for Parents*. The Hospital for Sick Children, 2003.

Williams, Donna. *Nobody Nowhere: The Extraordinary Autobiography of an Autistic*. Times Books, 1992.

Williams, Donna. *Somebody Somewhere: Breaking Free from the World of Autism*. Doubleday Canada, 1995.

Wilson, F. Paul. *The Touch*. G. P. Putnam's Sons, 1986.

Autism Society, Newfoundland Labrador

In 1982, Autism Society Canada (ASC) held a meeting in St. John's with the purpose of starting a chapter there. Barbara Hopkins, professor of education at Memorial University of Newfoundland, was invited to join ASC's board of directors in 1983. Her mission was to create a chapter in St. John's. A constitution and bylaws were drafted in 1987, and the Autism Society, Newfoundland Labrador (ASNL) was formally incorporated under the Newfoundland and Labrador Companies Act and registered as a charity under the Income Tax Act.

The capital campaign to build a provincial autism centre officially began in 2003, with Craig and Elaine Dobbin as major benefactors. The doors opened in late 2005, but what would become the Elaine Dobbin Centre for Autism officially opened in June 2006 to serve the Avalon Region. Other regional centres soon followed: the first regional office opened in 2009 in Grand Falls–Windsor to serve the South Central Region; the second opened in 2010 in Clarenville–Shoal Harbour to serve the Eastern Region; and the third opened in 2011 in Corner Brook to serve the Western Region.

The Autism Society, Newfoundland and Labrador's programs, services, and supports run from advocacy, on behalf of those people with autism spectrum disorder (ASD) along with their families and caregivers, to outreach programs and employment opportunities. The goal of programming and outreach is to offer supports to clients in and around the St. John's Metro area and to provide learning and growth opportunities in all areas of the province. Services are delivered from a staffed office with program space, each with a regional assistant manager, in the Avalon, Eastern, South Central, and Western regions.

INDEX

Visit Flanker Press at:

www.flankerpress.com

https://www.facebook.com/flankerpress

https://twitter.com/FlankerPress

http://www.youtube.com/user/FlankerPress